MYplace

FOR BIBLE STUDY

Published by First Place for Health
Galveston, Texas, USA
www.firstplaceforhealth.com
Printed in the USA

ISBN: 978-1-942425-46-5

CONTENTS

MY PLACE FOR BIBLE STUDY

A Better Way

Foreword by Vicki Heath 4
About the Author / About the Contributor .5
Introduction 7

Week One: Lose Your Life to Find It 9
Week Two: Be Weak to Become Strong 23
Week Three: Give Away to Receive 37
Week Four: Be Hungry to Become Satisfied. 53
Week Five: Serve to Be Honored. 69
Week Six: Walk by Faith instead of by Sight 85
Week Seven: Embrace Trials to Become Joyful. 102
Week Eight: Seek First the Kingdom. 118
Week Nine: A Time to Celebrate. 136

Leader Discussion Guide 138
Jump Start Menus and Recipes 144
Steps for Spiritual Growth. 166
    God's Word for Your Life. 166
    Establishing a Quiet Time 168
    Sharing Your Faith 172
First Place for Health Member Survey .175
Personal Weight and Measurement Record 177
Weekly Prayer Partner Forms 179
Live It Trackers 197
100-Mile Club 215
Let's Count Our Miles 217

FOREWORD

I was introduced to First Place for Health in 1993 by my mother-in-law, who had great concern for the welfare of her grandchildren. I was overweight and overwrought! God used that first Bible study to start me on my journey to health, wellness, and a life of balance.

Our desire at First Place for Health is for you to begin that same journey. We want you to experience the freedom that comes from an intimate relationship with Jesus Christ and witness His love for you through reading your Bible and through prayer. To this end, we have designed each day's study (which will take about fifteen to twenty minutes to complete) to help you discover the deep truths of the Bible. Also included is a weekly Bible memory verse to help you hide God's Word in your heart. As you start focusing on these truths, God will begin a great work in you.

At the beginning of Jesus' ministry, when He was teaching from the book of Isaiah, He said to the people, "The Spirit of the Lord is on me, because he has anointed me to preach good news to the poor. He has sent me to proclaim freedom for the prisoners and recovery of sight for the blind, to release the oppressed, to proclaim the year of the Lord's favor" (Luke 4:18–19). Jesus came to set us free—whether that is from the chains of compulsivity, addiction, gluttony, overeating, under eating, or just plain unbelief. It is our prayer that He will bring freedom to your heart so you may experience abundant life.

God bless you as you begin this journey toward a life of liberty.

Vicki Heath, First Place for Health National Director

ABOUT THE AUTHOR

Debbie Behling is a writer and educator. She has authored two Bible studies for First Place for Health: *The Joy Adventure* and *God My Refuge*. She joined First Place for Health in 1981 and has led numerous groups, including her current group which began in 2005. For nineteen years she taught middle school students, and for ten years she taught high school students online. She authored and edited over thirty publications starting in 2003 with Region 4 Education Service Center in Houston. This thirty-five-year educator has presented at conferences at the local, state, national, and international levels and designed and delivered professional development sessions. She has a B.A. from Dallas Baptist College with a triple major in secondary education, history, and psychology and a M.Ed. from Northwestern University Natchitoches focused on educational technology. She has two children and one grandchild, and she lives with her husband in Sugar Land, Texas, along with their miniature dachshunds. She enjoys singing, reading, scrapbooking, and genealogy. You can find her on social media at @bdebsing.

ABOUT THE CONTRIBUTOR

Lisa Lewis, who provided the menus and recipes in this study, is the author of *Healthy Happy Cooking*. Lisa's cooking skills have been a part of First Place for Health wellness weeks and other events for many years. She provided recipes for seventeen of the First Place for Health Bible studies and is a contributing author in *Better Together* and *Healthy Holiday Living*. She partners with community networks, including the Real Food Project, to bring healthy cooking classes to underserved areas. She is dedicated to bringing people together around the dinner table with healthy, delicious meals that are easy to prepare. Lisa lives in Galveston and is married to John. They have three children: Tal, Hunter, and Harper. Visit www.healthyhappycook.com for more delicious inspiration.

INTRODUCTION

First Place for Health is a Christ-centered health program that emphasizes balance in the physical, mental, emotional, and spiritual areas of life. The First Place for Health program is meant to be a daily process. As we learn to keep Christ first in our lives, we will find that He is the One who satisfies our hunger and our every need.

This Bible study is designed to be used in conjunction with the First Place for Health program but can be beneficial for anyone interested in obtaining a balanced lifestyle. The Bible study has been created in a seven-day format, with the last two days reserved for reflection on the material studied. Keep in mind that the ultimate goal of studying the Bible is not only for knowledge but also for application and a changed life. Don't feel anxious if you can't seem to find the correct answer. Many times, the Word will speak differently to different people, depending on where they are in their walk with God and the season of life they are experiencing. Be prepared to discuss with your fellow First Place for Health members what you learned that week through your study.

There are some additional components included with this study that will be helpful as you pursue the goal of giving Christ first place in every area of your life:

○ **Leader Discussion Guide:** This discussion guide is provided to help the First Place for Health leader guide a group through this Bible study. It includes ideas for facilitating a First Place for Health class discussion for each week of the Bible study.

○ **Jump Start Recipes:** There are seven days of recipes--breakfast, lunch and dinner-- to get you started.

○ **Steps for Spiritual Growth:** This section will provide you with some basic tips for how to memorize Scripture and make it a part of your life, establish a quiet time with God each day, and share your faith with others..

○ **First Place for Health Member Survey:** Fill this out and bring it to your first meeting. This information will help your leader know your interests and talents.

○ **Personal Weight and Measurement Record:** Use this form to keep a record of your weight loss. Record any loss or gain on the chart after the weigh-in at each week's meeting.

○ **Weekly Prayer Partner Forms:** Fill out this form before class and place it into a basket during the class meeting. After class, you will draw out a prayer request form, and this will be your prayer partner for the week. Try to call or email the person sometime before the next class meeting to encourage that person.

○ **100-Mile Club:** A worthy goal we encourage is for you to complete 100 miles of exercise during your twelve weeks in First Place for Health. There are many activities listed on pages 265-266 that count toward your goal of 100 miles and a handy tracker to track your miles.

○ **Live It Trackers:** Your Live It Tracker is to be completed at home and turned in to your leader at your weekly First Place for Health meeting. The Tracker is designed to help you practice mindfulness and stay accountable with regard to your eating and exercise habits.

WEEK ONE: LOSE YOUR LIFE TO FIND IT

SCRIPTURE MEMORY VERSE
If you cling to your life, you will lose it; but if you give up your life for me, you will find it. Matthew 10:39 NLT

In 1999 a film exploded on movie screens called The Matrix. Thomas Anderson was shocked to discover that the world in which he lived was actually a simulated reality. Machines had designed a program that trapped all humanity in a lie. He could only access the real world by swallowing a red pill and when he did, his perspective was forever changed. The world in which he now lived, along with others who fought against the false world, was the true reality.

When Jesus came to earth, He preached about the true reality: the Kingdom of God. It was a revolutionary message that shook the culture of His time. He taught that we should love our enemies, turn the other cheek, and practice humble servanthood. And He modeled this lifestyle perfectly. But His message was not accepted by everyone, and those in authority had Him executed. Yet in true upside-down Kingdom fashion, Jesus Christ defeated death by dying, then rising from the dead, completely conquering sin and death. He gives us the opportunity to reject the lies of this corrupted world and access the real world God created, one of grace and mercy, forgiveness and peace.

The Kingdom of God is upside down from our world and our natural instincts. We want to satisfy our physical hungers, but God says to hunger after righteousness. You likely joined First Place for Health to shed pounds, and this program provides powerful tools to become physically healthier. But you may find that God will take your desire to lose weight and transform it into a desire to gain more of Him. And in the process, you will lose weight as well.

How do we live in the upside-down Kingdom of God today? How can the lessons of the Kingdom that Jesus taught relate to our healthy choices and wellness journey? This study, *A Better Way*, explores answers to these questions, searching the Scriptures in general and Jesus' teachings specifically, to discover better ways to live as Kingdom seekers.

—— DAY 1: DYING TO LIVE

Today I look to You, Father, for everything I need. I am nothing without You. I want to hear Your voice as I open Your Word right now.

God had a perfect plan for His creation. He took a formless void and transformed it into a place full of life and beauty. His crowning achievement was humanity. What does the Bible say about His accomplishment in Genesis 1:27?

_____

_____

_____

Being created in God's image means we are His physical representatives on earth. What did God say about making physical images to worship in Exodus 20:4-6?

_____

_____

_____

We don't need to make images of God; He already did that! We are His images, not to be worshiped but to be His light-bearers and partners in ruling His creation. But our image is tarnished by sin. What does Romans 3:23 say about our condition?

_____

_____

_____

Since the beginning people have tried various ways to earn their way back to a right relationship with God. But it is not humanly possible. Only God could provide the solution to salvation. Romans 6:23 gives us both bad news and good news. What does it say?

_____

_____

_____

God's better way of dying to live was modeled best by Jesus, Who gave up His earthly life to give us eternal life. We receive this life through faith in Him, and we learn to die to our own fleshly desires as they are replaced with His Spirit's life-giving power. His gift of love is free to us. We only have to accept it. But once we do, life in the real world begins. We lose our life to Him so we can gain the life we were created to live.

Thank You, Father, for Your amazingly generous gift of Jesus's death that pays the debt for my sin. I walk in freedom because I trust You for salvation rather than myself. Amen.

—— DAY 2: SACRIFICE TO SAVE

Praise You, Father, for Your mighty power and loving ways. My heart is open to Your teaching for today; quiet my mind as I focus only on You.

Because of sin, I am disconnected from a holy God. In true upside-down Kingdom fashion, God Himself provides the enigmatic solution: we live because Jesus died. What did Jesus say about this amazing gift in John 5:24?

_____

_____

_____

In Luke 19:10 Jesus states His mission. Write your name in the blank below.

For the Son of Man came to seek and to save _____, who was lost.

How can Jesus provide the solution to my lost condition? Read these verses and record what Jesus did to accomplish our salvation.

Scripture	What Jesus Did to Accomplish Our Salvation
Matthew 26:28	
2 Corinthians 5:21	
1 Peter 2: 21-24	

How would you describe what Jesus did to offer salvation to you?

_____

_____

_____

In his study *3:16: Numbers of Hope*, Max Lucado gives a startling illustration.

Christ gave Himself for you. Specifically, He exchanged hearts with you. This would be like the cardiologist who examined your test results saying, "Yes, your condition looks really bad, but I have a treatment. I'm going to exchange hearts. Mine is sturdy; yours is frail. Mine is pure; yours is diseased. Take mine and enjoy its vigor, and I'll take yours." Mind you, this is not a transplant; it's a swap.[1]

Have you accepted God's heart swap? If so, thank Him and praise Him for His indescribable gift! If you haven't yet, talk to your leader, a trusted friend, or God Himself. A new heart is waiting just for you.

God, it is beyond my understanding that You would give Your Son to die for my sins. Your love for me is boundless! Thank You for sending Jesus to be sin for me so I can know You as my Lord. Amen.

—— DAY 3: SOLD OUT
This is the day You have made, God, for Your pleasure and purposes. I rejoice in Your creation and the life You give me in Christ. I want to know You more.

Accepting Christ's gift of salvation is just the beginning of your new life. Our memory verse has an important paradox about this life. Fill in the blanks as you practice this week's memory verse.

If you _____ to your life, you will _____ it; but if you _____ _____ your life for Me, you will _____ it. Matthew _____

God calls us to be completely sold out to Him. He doesn't save us then expect us to live by our own efforts without Him at the helm. As we work on our fitness goals, it is easy to depend on ourselves for will power. I personally have not done well with my own will power. It is not enough to consistently overcome temptations to make unhealthy choices. God's power is my source of strength for victory. Writer David DePra puts it this way: "Jesus is warning against the tendency for Christians to try to control the outcome of their walk with Christ through the efforts of religious flesh."[2]

Let's explore how we can become completely sold out to God. Read Romans 12:1. What is the first word? _____

Therefore refers to the previous chapter concerning God's grace and mercy for all people. His grace doesn't require us to earn our salvation, but once we are saved, we begin a new process called *sanctification*. Every day we respond to God's grace with some measure of devotion and a passion to obey Him. What does verse 1 indicate about our response?

_____

_____

_____

The Jewish religion and many others require sacrifices to receive atonement. But Jesus has already paid the penalty for us. Instead of sacrificing to *become saved*, we sacrifice *because we are saved*. We crave healthy choices in response to the love God has given us and the movement of the Holy Spirit in our hearts. This is our "true and proper worship." Our food and exercise choices can be worshipful experiences because we are sacrificing our own desires to God.

How does Philippians 2:12-13 explain this process of sanctification?

_____

_____

_____

Sanctification is serious business but it is all from God: His purpose and His power. Living a sacrificial life is not a simple "one and done" kind of existence. We must constantly communicate and connect with God, the power source of our healthy living. What daily routines do you practice that keep you linked to God?

_____

_____

_____

What hinders you from close fellowship with God?

_____

_____

_____

DePra has also written, "If I try to save myself, I am denying Christ."[3] Christ's sacrifice has saved me; now I live for Him and not myself.

Lord, I confess that I do not always access Your power and purposes in my daily life. I crawl up on the altar of sacrifice, then I crawl down again to make my own choices. I know Your way is best, and I desire to be consistently yielded to You, through Your strength alone. Amen.

—— DAY 4: LIVING A CRUCIFIED LIFE

I seek You, Father, to learn how to live a healthy, balanced life. I cannot live without the power of Your Spirit in me. Fill me anew as we meet together now.

The paradox of dying to live is encapsulated in Galatians 2:19-20. Read these verses and fill in the blanks below.

For through the _____ I died to the _____
so that I might _____ for _____ . I have
been _____ with _____ and I no longer _____ , but _____ lives in me. The
life I now _____ in the _____ , I live by
_____ in the _____ _____
_____ for me.

A central tenet of Jesus' teachings involved this idea of dying to live. Look up Matthew 16:24-26 and summarize the challenge Jesus presents to His disciples.

_____

_____

_____

This Kingdom concept is upside-down: dying to live. How is that possible? It only happens when the Spirit of God lives inside of us. It only happens when we allow God's Spirit to direct us and empower us. We are not robots but dynamically connected to God through His Spirit, actively engaging with Him to live a crucified life.

How devoted are you to following Jesus? Paul wrote about his own passion for Christ in Philippians 3:7-8. Read these verses and describe his commitment.

_____

_____

_____

Do I value my relationship with Christ in that way? Do I love Jesus more than my own desires for the food I want to eat? Eating more than we need or using food for emotional comfort is a common practice for many. This habit can lead to overweight, physical ailments, and psychological distress. We are living to die rather than dying to live. Jesus calls us into a better way: dying to our fleshly desires and living as He leads, following Him rather than our own ways. He invites me to choose His ways and leave my own ways behind, as if I had left them nailed to the cross. In my eating habits He wants me to choose life-giving food rather than food that affects my body in harmful ways. That's what our First Place for Health food plan is about: the better way of choosing food that enhances our health rather than choosing food that destroys it.

Do you have a desire for a specific food that interferes with your fitness goals? Sweets are a real problem for me for a lot of reasons, primarily because they taste really good! I constantly ask God to help me control my sweet tooth. I have strategies to help me resist temptation, but what I really want is for God to completely erase my desires for them. My battle keeps me on my knees and seeking Him daily. Do you have a food-related fight? If so, what is it?

_____

_____

_____

Barb Roose addresses this subject in her book *Surrendered*. She says that the battle to retain control of our lives is actually counterproductive. "I realized that the harder I held on, the heavier the weight (of my problems) became. ... The act of surrender is an invitation to release our problems to God and receive His provision, protection, and peace in return."[4] By allowing God to rule in our lives, we actually have more control rather than less.

Giving my desires to God and asking Him to replace them with His are part of living a crucified life. The better way is to allow God to fill us with Himself so there is no room for our desires for unhealthy things.

God, You know my struggles with doing things my own way. I want to follow You completely, but at times I choose what I want instead. Help me to be completely surrendered to You and Your ways. I nail my desires to the cross and leave them there. Amen.

—— DAY 5: OWNERSHIP
How holy and blessed to come to You now, my Father, to sit at Your feet and learn from You. I am ready to listen and enjoy this time in Your precious Word.

Every time I start a new First Place for Health Bible study, the first thing I do is write my name in the front of my book. I learned to read before I went to kindergarten and have been a book lover ever since. Before electronic books, which I also love, my bookshelves were filled to overflowing with cherished volumes, all with my name written in the front. For me, there's something special about owning a book.

The ownership of our lives is an important question. Is it ours or God's? What does 2 Corinthians 1:21-22 tell us about who owns us?

_____

_____

_____

_____

Also read Ephesians 1:13-14. What else do you learn about the seal God has placed on us?

_____

_____

_____

_____

The word translated *seal* in these verses means "to put a mark on something to show possession, authority, identity, or security."[5] What does that mean to us as Christians, especially as we seek to consistently make healthy choices to meet our fitness goals? Read each of the scriptures below and record how they relate to you in terms of making healthy choices.

Truths	Scriptures	Relationship to Making Healthy Choices
God created me.	Psalm 100:3	
I belong to God.	John 10:28-29	
He sacrificed His Son to redeem my life for Himself.	Romans 5:8	
He cares for me as a cherished member of His family.	Galatians 4:4-7	

Although we belong to God through faith in Christ, we may put up some No Trespassing signs in our lives. We may have areas we want to keep hidden from Jesus. They may be painful or shameful, and we don't want even our loving Lord to expose them. Or perhaps there are areas of our heart that we still want to control ourselves rather than release them to God.

Understanding more about God's character may help us to allow Him into these restricted areas. Read Exodus 34:6 and list at least five things God says about His character.

_____

_____

_____

God is not a mean boss who wants to make me do things to torture me for His own amusement, but a loving Father Who created me and knows what is best for me and Who wants to develop me into the best version of the person He created me to be. I will find my greatest satisfaction, purpose, and joy in giving myself completely into His care. I can trust Him with my deepest secrets and most humiliating defeats.

Consider what part or parts of your life that you are keeping from God's loving and forgiving eyes. What can you do this week to begin the process of allowing Him into these hidden areas?

_____

_____

_____

Whose name is written on the first page of your life's story? I'm thankful I accepted God's autograph in my book of life early on, and I continue to ask Him to write my story as the Author and Finisher of my faith.

I am Yours, dear God, and I rejoice that You have redeemed me and adopted me into Your heavenly family. You are compassionate, gracious, slow to anger, loving, and faithful. May I wear Your Name proudly and authentically as I allow Your leadership in making Your healthiest choices each day. Amen.

—— DAY 6: REFLECTION AND APPLICATION

Oh, Lord, You are my strength and my life. Every breath I take comes from You. I praise You for Your mighty works and Your love for me. Teach me Your truths.

Albert was born in Germany in 1875. He was bilingual and intelligent, yet he was also tender-hearted toward those in need. He earned a Ph.D., wrote a book, and was an accomplished musician. Certainly, he had a brilliant life ahead of him, full of academia and music. But he was not satisfied with the path his life was taking. Listen to his words.

The plan which I meant now to put into execution had been in my mind for a long time, having been conceived so long ago as my student days. It struck me as incomprehensible that I should be allowed to lead such a happy life, which I saw so many people around me wrestling with care and suffering... Then one brilliant summer morning at Günsbach, during the Whitsuntide holidays—it was in 1896— there came to me, as I awoke, the thought that I must not accept this happiness as a matter of course, but must give something in return for it. Proceeding to think the matter out at once with calm deliberation, while the birds were singing out- side, I settled with myself before I got up, that I would consider myself justified in living till I was thirty for science and art, in order to devote myself from that time forward to the direct service of humanity. Many a time already had I tried to settle what meaning lay hidden for me in the saying of Jesus! "Whosoever would save his life shall lose it, and whosoever shall lose his life for My sake and the Gospel shall save it."[6]

Albert Schweitzer went on to medical school and after eight years, he became a missionary to Africa. For 50 years he and his wife served in Africa, seeking to meet the medical needs of people there and returning to Europe occasionally to raise money for his hospital. He later received the Nobel Peace Prize "for his altruism, reverence for life, and tireless humanitarian work which has helped making the idea of brotherhood between men and nations a living one."[7] He died at age 90 on the mission field in Africa. His life is certainly an excellent example of dying to live.

God may not call you in the same way He did Albert Schweitzer, but He calls each of us to lay down our lives for His sake and live for Him instead of ourselves. How has God called you and/or how is God calling you now to give up your life to Him?

_____

_____

_____

Holy Lord, my life is in Your hands. I give it up willingly to You, for You have loved me beyond belief, delivered me from despair, and offered me new life through Jesus Christ. Take my life, Lord, and use it for Your glory. Amen.

—— DAY 7: REFLECTION AND APPLICATION

I need You now, Lord, because life in this world is exhausting. I am torn between following You wholly and giving in to my own desires. Use this time to transform my heart.

Practice this week's memory verse by writing here:

_____

_____

This week we have explored God's better way of dying to live, one of scripture's great paradoxes. We are faced with the choice, sometimes daily and sometimes at crucial moments, to die to ourselves and obey God or try to exist through our own power. What impacts the difference in making that choice?

There are at least three things we can do to put ourselves in the best place to choose God over self. Each of these are part of our practices in First Place for Health.

- **Constant prayer:** Talking to God at specified times and throughout the day keeps us connected to the source of life.
- **Continual Bible reading**: Reading God's Word daily and the whole Bible in a year regularly feeds our spirits and builds our faith.
- **Consistent Bible study**: Digging into God's Word gives the Spirit opportunities to apply it to our lives. This practice includes memorizing scripture.

How are you doing on these three practices? What can you do this week to progress in your faithfulness to prayer and God's Word?

_____

_____

_____

During this study you will be challenged to consider Jesus' radical teachings about His better way. This week's topic is the first of many paradoxical paradigms He gave to His disciples. Spend time meditating on this idea of dying to live, allowing God to speak to you and asking Him questions you have about what it means in your life. There is space here to journal if you wish. Don't feel pressured to fill the entire space. Here are some possible prompts to get you started; choose one if you wish.

- Take any idea from this week's study and go deeper.

- Consider a food that is tempting to you and hard to resist, one that threatens to sabotage your fitness goals. Write a letter to this food, telling it that you are choosing God's better way of sacrifice and refusing to give in to its temptations. You could draw an altar and sketch or paste an image of the food, illustrating your desire to sacrifice your hunger for this food to the Lord.

- Exodus 34:6 lists God's own description of His character: compassionate, gracious, slow to anger, abounding in steadfast love, and faithfulness. Identify ways God has shown His character to you in each of these ways. List them or use images in your journal. Write a prayer of thanks to Him for His character and the ways He has expressed these characteristics to you.

• Find a song that encourages you in this process. You may document the lyrics and record your own reflections on them, or you could illustrate them with sketches or images you locate. Two examples for this week's study are "To Live Is Christ" by Sidewalk Prophets (2015) and "Dying to Live" by To/Die/For (1998).

Your journal holds a very private and personal process; therefore, share it carefully. If social media is a healthy place for you, use these hashtags for posting your words, images, other reflections, or personal stories from this study: #fp4h and #fp4habetterway. You can view my journal and others' entries using these hashtags.

May I pray over you as together we consider God's better way? Please put your name in the blanks below. Consider saying the prayer aloud and repeat it whenever you desire.

Heavenly Father, thank you for _____ who loves You and desires to know You more. As we go through this study, give _____ a deeper hunger for You. Empower _____ to hear Your words through Your Holy Spirit's work and encourage _____ to use these teachings every day in _____'s life. _____ agrees with You that living in Your Kingdom is the best way to live. Yet _____ knows that it can only be done in Your power. Help _____ to yield to you more each day as _____ seeks You first and wants to love You with all _____'s being. You have given Your all for _____; _____ wants to give all to You. _____ prays all these things in the strong name of Jesus, Who perfectly modeled this life of sacrifice. Amen.

1 Max Lucado, The Heart He Offers (Video 3), 3:16 Online Bible Study with Max Lucado (Nashville: HarperCollins Christian Publishing, 2022).

2 David DePra, "Losing Your Life to Find It," The Good News (1999), https://www.goodnewsarticles.com/Mar99-1.htm.

3 David DePra, "Losing Your Life."

4 Barb Roose, Surrendered (Nashville: Abingdon Press, 2020),[12] .

5 Step Bible. 2 Corinthians 1: https://www.stepbible.org/?q=reference=2Cor.1|version=NASB2020&options=VNHUG.

6 Brent Werjoski, "Philosophy of Civilization, Pt 1, Albert Schweitzer." (2014),: http://brentwejrowski.com/2014/02/24/philosophy-of-civilization-pt1.html.

7 "Albert Schweitzer—Facts - Facts,"." (2022). Nobel Prize Facts (2022), : . https://www.nobelprize.org/prizes/peace/1952/schweitzer/facts/.

WEEK TWO: BE WEAK TO BECOME STRONG

SCRIPTURE MEMORY VERSE

Blessed are the meek, for they will inherit the earth. Matthew 5:5

Some of the electricity you use every day may come from a hydroelectric source, typically through a dam. The dam uses a strong structure to hold back water from flowing on its own. Through the force of gravity, water is directed to flow and turn machinery that converts the power into electricity. On its own the water couldn't provide electrical power, but the dam system is able to harness the power of flowing water and create energy that we can use in our homes and businesses.

God is *the* power source, the Creator of the universe and the Sustainer of life. He wants to provide His power to us as we allow the Holy Spirit to flow through us, giving us spiritual energy and abundant life. On our own, we have no power to fully follow Jesus or consistently conquer the temptations to make unhealthy choices.

Last week in *A Better Way*, we looked at these ideas about dying to live.

- Jesus died so we can live; we access His gift of eternal life through faith in Him.
- Jesus offers to swap our sin-sick hearts with His pure heart.
- After salvation we continue to follow Christ and become transformed or sanctified.
- Giving my desires to God and asking Him to replace them with His is part of living a crucified life.
- We find our greatest satisfaction, purpose, and joy in giving ourselves completely into God's care.

This week's lesson considers another paradox of the upside-down Kingdom of God that Jesus taught during His time on earth. How can I be weak and become strong at the same time? How can God's strength empower me to make healthy choices when my own willpower is inadequate to conquer temptation? We'll explore meekness and see how Jesus modeled it for us while conquering sin and death through God's strength.

—— DAY 1: WEAKNESS VERSUS MEEKNESS

Thank You, Father, that Your Word is a lamp for my feet and a light for my path. You show me Your goodness and guidance in every passage of scripture I read. Give me wisdom as You speak to me today.

Write this week's memory verse here.

_____

_____

_____

What comes to your mind when you encounter the word *meek*? For many, this word has a negative connotation, evoking images of people who have no backbone and allow others to walk all over them. But this modern use of *meek* differs from the word's meaning in the Bible. The Greek word for *meek* in Matthew 5:5 contains the idea of gentleness: "the positive moral quality of dealing with people in a kind manner, with humility and consideration."[1] Another expression of the word is "decided strength of disciplined calmness."[2] Others have defined it as "strength under control."

Jesus consistently modeled this quality. Read each scripture below and record how He exemplified meekness.

Scripture	How Jesus Modeled Meekness
Matthew 4:1-11	
Matthew 26:50-53	
John 13:3-5	
Philippians 2:5-8	

Read Hebrews 4:15. How is Jesus's meekness described?

_____

Jesus *laid aside* everything He had: power, glory, a throne in heaven. He *limited* His divine power so He could take on human flesh and live as we do. He *allowed* Himself to be tortured and killed so we could receive salvation and enjoy relationship with a holy God. He perfectly *obeyed* God and did things His way: "The Son can do nothing by himself; he can do only what he sees his Father doing, because whatever the Father does the Son also does" (John 5:19). His strength came from God as He *yielded* to His authority.

The original use of the word used in Matthew 5:5 for *meek* referred to a horse in a Greek play. In this story the horse was highly spirited and refused to be broken. Although it was the fastest and strongest horse, its vitality was ineffective because it would not submit to its trainer.[3] We too have potential power as children of the omnipotent God, but that power is only available as we humbly allow Him to work through us, training us to become all He created us to be.

Many of us struggle with wanting to do things our own way when it comes to fitness. We want to eat the foods we like even if they are not the best choice for us, and we don't want to exercise consistently. Like the horse, we don't want to submit to our Trainer, our God Who loves us and knows what's best for us. The answer to this conflict is meekness, submitting to Him and allowing Him to empower us to make healthy choices. How can this concept of meekness help you in your process to reach your fitness goals?

_____

_____

_____

Thank You for Your mighty power, Lord, which energizes me through Jesus my Lord. May I consistently submit to You, allowing You to work in and through me to accomplish Your will. I know alone I am weak, but with You, I am strong. Amen.

—— DAY 2: THE SOURCE OF STRENGTH

I need Your strength today, Lord, to face the challenges before me. In this quiet time, pour out Your Holy Spirit on me to teach and guide me.

Review yesterday's study and write your own definition of meekness.

_____

_____

_____

How do we develop this characteristic of meekness? First, we must know its source.

Read Ephesians 3:16-17 and list two sources of strength.

_____

_____

_____

You have likely learned the meaning of the word "love" used in this passage and other places in the New Testament. God's kind of love is not emotional but behavioral: doing what is best for others even if it requires personal sacrifice. Based on what we learned about meekness yesterday, we can see how love incorporates meekness by putting aside self and focusing on another's needs. Read John 15:13. How does Jesus describe this kind of love?

_____

_____

_____

According to 1 John 3:16 what evidence of love did Jesus and His followers exemplify?

_____

_____

_____

The second source of strength is the Holy Spirit. Look up John 14:15-16 and John 16:8. What roles does the Holy Spirit serve in our lives?

_____

_____

_____

Additionally, what does Acts 1:8 say that the Holy Spirit empowers us to do?

_____

_____

_____

Read Romans 8:26-27. How does the Spirit help us and how does this ministry relate to developing meekness in us?

_____

_____

_____

Finally, look up 2 Timothy 1:7. What does the Spirit of God give us?

_____

_____

_____

How do the three things in 2 Timothy 1:7 relate to developing meekness?

_____

_____

_____

As we submit to God's work within us through His Holy Spirit, we become meek, leaning on Him for strength. That process results in love for others. How is God's Spirit currently working in you to produce meekness? How do you see His work in you creating love for others?

_____

_____

_____

Father, thank You for Your incredible love for me and for all people. You demonstrated Your love by sending Christ to die for me while I was in rebellion against You, before I even knew You. And you have sent Your own Spirit to live in me to teach, guide, and empower me. May Your love flow through me to others as Your Spirit leads. Amen.

—— DAY 3: PERFECTING POWER IN WEAKNESS

Holy Lord, You are the giver of life and all good things. I want to know You more today than I did yesterday. As You impart Your Word to me, open my understanding and deepen my desire for You.

I learned sign language when I was in college, and I enjoyed being a part of my church's deaf community. One of the interpreters told us a story about flying on a plane. He pretended to be hearing-impaired so he could experience how other people responded to the deaf. He learned a great deal about how deaf people were treated, and it increased his empathy and understanding of their lives. He felt that putting himself in their shoes helped him be better as an interpreter and a friend of deaf people.

Jesus did something even more radical than pretending to be human. He became human. How does John 1:14 describe this phenomenon?

_____

_____

_____

The verse literally reads "He spread a tent" or "encamped" among us. The Jews of John's time would understand this wording in light of the Old Testament tent of meeting from their ancestors' time following the Exodus. The purpose of that tent or tabernacle was to meet with God. First, they had to follow rituals of sacrificing animals and going through a high priest to access God's presence, and even then that access was quite limited. But Jesus brought a better way to come to God, because He *became* the tabernacle and the sacrifice for us. Now the way to God was wide open. Ephesians 2:18 says, "For through him we both have access to the Father by one Spirit."

Hebrews 2:18 tells us about Jesus' empathy for us. What does it say?

_____

_____

_____

The high priest represented God to the Israelite people and the people to God. He would go into the tent of meeting to offer sacrifices on behalf of the people so they could stand before God in His righteousness. Jesus became our new and permanent high priest, and Hebrews 4:14-16 tells us about His role. Read these verses and fill in the blanks below.

14 – Since Jesus is our high priest, let us hold firmly to _____.

15 – Jesus is able to empathize with our _____.

15 – He was _____ in every way, just as we are—yet He did not _____.

16 – Let us approach God's throne of _____ with _____, so that we may receive _____ and _____ to help us in our time of _____.

These truths help us understand how Jesus modeled meekness for us. He limited His power and allowed Himself to be tempted because He wanted to understand how we face the challenge of temptation. He is authentic in His relationship with us. When I tell Him how hard it is to resist temptation and make healthy choices, He knows what I'm talking about. And although I can never reach His level of perfect sinlessness, He gives me hope and encouragement to lean on Him for strength rather than trying to succeed in my own power.

Paul wrote about his experience with meekness. Read 2 Corinthians 12:9-10 and summarize Paul's discovery about God's strength.

_____

_____

_____

How do these truths help you understand meekness? How can these truths impact your fitness journey?

_____

_____

_____

Thank You, Jesus, for becoming human so You can truly understand the challenges I face. I am learning more about meekness and want to embrace this godly character trait. Work in me to trade in my weakness for Your strength, which is sufficient for all my needs. Amen.

—— DAY 4: STAND STILL

Quiet my mind and heart, Lord, as I spend these moments with You. My life is full of busyness and distractions, which can disturb my focus on You. I lay them aside now, so I can hear Your voice.

Imagine you are hiking in the wild and come upon a grizzly bear. What should you do? Your first instinct is likely to scream and run. But the bear will probably be able to run faster than you. Experts say you should remain composed and stand still. Standing still communicates to the bear that you are not a danger to his safety. You may talk calmly to let it know you are human and not a threat.[4] This approach sounds difficult to do when faced with a terrifying beast! But it is the best action to take.

There are times in our faith walk when God wants us to stand still. It may seem like a passive position and difficult to do when circumstances threaten us like a scary grizzly bear. But in these moments our meekness gives us opportunities to watch God work in amazing ways.

Moses experienced this truth dramatically. In Egypt he demanded that Pharaoh let the Israelite people go, but Pharaoh refused. Ten times God sent a plague; after the tenth plague, Pharaoh agreed to allow the Israelites to leave. Moses led them out of slavery and toward the Promised Land. Imagine the excitement and celebration as the people packed up their belongings and left their slavery behind them.

But they found themselves surrounded by danger because Pharaoh had changed his mind and led his army to bring them back. His army marched behind them. In front of them the Red Sea blocked their escape. Around them were other nations who were not friendly to them. They were in an impossible situation.

What did the people say to Moses in Exodus 14:11-12?

_____

_____

_____

What did Moses tell them to do in response to the threats surrounding them (verses 13-14)?

_____

_____

_____

Circle the words stand *firm*, *still*, or similar words in your response above. You know the rest of the story. God delivered the Israelites by parting the Red Sea, opening a way of deliverance from the Egyptian army. And He destroyed the Egyptians when they tried to follow the Israelites through the Red Sea. I am confident that Moses and the Israelites didn't see that coming!

Have you ever been in this kind of situation? There seems to be no way out. You cry out to the Lord for help, and His response is that you should stand still. I have experienced this many times. I found myself in a situation where someone I love was in dire need, and I could do nothing to help. I felt powerless and impotent. All I could do was cry out to the Lord and wait for His deliverance. He was faithful to send help from other sources while I stood still and trusted Him.

The Israelites celebrated their deliverance with the first recorded song of worship in the Bible (Exodus 15). They had encountered God in a powerful way, and they had reason to trust Him more. But God had additional reasons for leading His people through this impossible mission. Read Exodus 14:4 and identify God's objective for the Red Sea experience.

_____

_____

_____

God may want to use your Red Sea situation to impact someone. You may never know how your meekness may influence others. Standing still seems weak, but when we are still, the omnipotent God of the universe can display His majesty and glory apart from our actions. Meekness is really a position of power because of God's supremacy.

Have you experienced standing still and watching God work in the past? What grizzly bear threatens you today? What would standing still look like in this circumstance? Share your story here.

_____

_____

_____

Mighty God, You are glorious and full of majesty. Your power is unlimited and Your ways are always best. Help me to know when to stand still so I can see Your deliverance. I know You will fight for me while I trust You for the victory. Amen.

—— DAY 5: INHERIT THE EARTH

You are full of love and mercy, my Father. I want more of You, and I seek Your presence right now. Open Your Word to me so I may know Your precious truths.

In the Beatitudes, Jesus mentioned meekness as a characteristic of those who follow Him. Read Matthew 5:5, this week's memory verse, and write it here.

_____

_____

There are two parts to each Beatitude. First, we are blessed if we are meek. On Day 1 we looked at some definitions of meekness. Here is another one: "Meekness is therefore an active and deliberate acceptance of undesirable circumstances that are wisely seen by the individual as only part of a larger picture. Meekness is not a resignation to fate, a passive and reluctant submission to events."[5] How does this definition fit in with what you have learned so far about meekness?

_____

_____

_____

One thing we know from this study is that meekness is a choice I can make as a follower of Jesus. It is not being crushed by circumstances into an inactive state but a decision to trust in God and wait for His answer to my situation. It is recognizing my weakness and choosing faith in God for my strength. And the more I do that, the greater will be my resilience to face more impossible situations in the future. For there will be more.

At times the word translated meekness is associated with gentleness or humility. Galatians 5:22-23 tell us that these qualities are a result of the work of the Holy Spirit in our lives as the fruit we bear. How do you see meekness in your own life, and how does it give you the opportunity to exhibit gentleness and humility?

_____

_____

_____

The second thing that Matthew 5:5 tells us is "The meek will inherit the earth." What does it mean to "inherit the earth?" The Greek word for _earth_ means "ground" or "land." Think about God's promise to Abraham concerning Canaan and the Promised Land the Israelites traveled to after the Exodus. Cultivating meekness means we understand that we are right where God wants us to be. He may have promised you something that you are not presently experiencing. You may have been promised healing but are sick. You may have been promised friendship but are lonely. You may have been promised influence but are unknown. The current lack of fulfillment of your promise doesn't mean it won't come. Your position while you wait, however, is crucial. And that position is trusting God while He develops your meekness. It is understanding that the current situation is necessary because of what God wants to accomplish in His Kingdom's work, which is the bigger picture. You _will_ inherit the earth, meaning you _will_ arrive at the place He has prepared for you, and you will arrive clothed in gentleness and humility rather than harshness and pride.

We can accept unpleasant or difficult circumstances because we know it is the better way of God's upside-down Kingdom. The King of Kings wants us to inherit the earth, but the way to rule is to submit to Him. Instead of trying to rule the earth through our own power, we put aside our own desire to rule and accept God's authority. We can release to God our need to feel in control, because He knows what He is doing. How can you submit to God today so He can develop meekness in you?

_____

_____

_____

Father, I bow my knee to Your loving authority, knowing that Your promises for me will be fulfilled. As I wait, I pray You will develop meekness in me so I can become all You want me to be. I claim the promised land that I will inherit because I learn meekness from You. Amen.

—— DAY 6: REFLECTION AND APPLICATION

God, You are my salvation and my portion forever. I trust in You alone for all that I need. Be my strength and my shield in my fitness journey as I learn meekness and dependence on You.

Joni Eareckson Tada, a quadriplegic author, artist, and speaker shared the following story.

When I was in Germany speaking at a church, a blind woman named Elizabeth served as my interpreter. You can imagine the two of us on stage—me with my wheelchair and Elizabeth with her white cane. During a break, someone placed an English language magazine on my lap. It looked like a good read, but with my quadriplegia, I couldn't hold the periodical or turn its pages. "Elizabeth," I said, "how 'bout if you hold the magazine and turn the pages, and I will read out loud. That way we can both enjoy it." And that's just what we did. I needed her; she needed me; and together we accomplished something that blessed both of us. That is how the body of Christ should work! Our combined weaknesses become delightful strengths.[6]

This is a beautiful illustration of meekness on the part of both Joni and Elizabeth. The great thing about meekness with God is that He is not weak at all. But pride and fear may cause us to struggle with standing still and watching Him accomplish His purposes.

What does Proverbs 25:27 say about meekness and how does it relate to making healthy food choices?

_____

_____

_____

Below is a chart with two columns, one titled "Me" and one titled "Meek." Consider how challenges on your fitness journey and your faith walk look when you are calling the shots but also when you are meek and allowing God full control of your being. An example is given.

Fitness Challenges	Me	Meek
Go out to eat	Choose what I want	Ask God to show me what to eat before I order

Without His power we are weak; with His power we can become meek.

When I'm faced with a decision, help me choose meekness over my own desires, dear Lord. I know Your way for me is always best, and my flesh struggles with choosing Your best over my selfish desires. Thank You for Your never-ending love and grace that thrills my soul. Amen.

—— DAY 7: REFLECTION AND APPLICATION

Oh Lord God, You have made the heavens and the earth by Your great power. Nothing is too difficult for You! How easy it should be for me to choose meekness and trust in You. Help my unbelief and show me how You want to work in me while I stand still.

Practice this week's memory verse here:

_____

_____

_____

This week we have explored Jesus' teaching about meekness and the paradox of how being weak can make us strong. God can do so much more in and through us when we are meek and lean on Him rather than take control of a situation and try to work it out in our own power without Him. In choosing the better way of meekness, God can take us to the place He has promised and prepared for us.

As you reflect on this week's study about meekness, consider one of the following journaling prompts. Spend time meditating on meekness, allowing God to speak to you and asking Him questions you have about what it means in your life. There is space here to journal if you wish.

• Take any idea from this week's study and go deeper.

• Choose one area of your fitness journey that you find especially difficult. Write about your struggle and ask God to show you where you can choose meekness instead of your own plans. Thank Him for His strength when you are weak.

• Create an acrostic with the word meekness. For example, write "meekness" in a vertical line on the left side and write a word or phrase starting with each letter that relates to meekness. For example, the M might be "my way submits to His way."

• Find a song that encourages you in this process. You may document the lyrics and record your own reflections on them, or you could illustrate them with sketches or images you locate. Two examples for this week's study are "Meekness and Majesty" by Graham Kendrick (2015) and "Gentle Like Jesus" by Joel Sczebel and Todd Twining (2009).

- Your journal is a very private and personal process; therefore, share it carefully. If social media is a healthy place for you, use these hashtags for posting your words, images, other reflections, or personal stories from this study: #fp4h and #fp4habetterway. You can view my journal and others' entries using these hashtags.

My strong and loving Lord, thank You for showing me more about following You with all my heart, soul, mind, and strength. I know I can trust You with every part of my life. Show me how I can choose your better way of meekness when I face challenges that I think I can handle on my own. I love You, Father, and cherish my life in You. Amen.

1 The Step Bible, https://www.stepbible.org/?q=reference=Matt.5|version=ESV&options=NHVUG.

2 Mark E. Caner. "Spiritual Meekness: An Imperative Virtue for Christian Leaders," Regents University (2010) - https://www.regent.edu/journal/inner-resources-for-leaders/spiritual-meekness-a-virtue-for-christian-leaders/.

3 Brent L. Bolin, "Meek—Christ the Great Example of Humility." Faith Bible Ministry Blog (2012), https://faithbibleministriesblog.com/2012/03/09/meek/.

4 "Staying Safe around Bears," National Park Service (2022), https://www.nps.gov/subjects/bears/safety.htm.

5 Samuel A. Meier, "Meekness," Baker's Evangelical Dictionary of Biblical Theology (1966), https://www.biblestudytools.com/dictionary/meekness/.

6 Joni Eareckson Tada, E. (2016). The Pastor's Workshop. "Sermon Illustrations on the Body of Christ." https://thepastorsworkshop.com/sermon-illustrations-on-the-body-of-christ/.

WEEK THREE: GIVE AWAY TO RECEIVE

SCRIPTURE MEMORY VERSE

Jesus said to him, "If you wish to be complete, go and sell your possessions and give to the poor, and you will have treasure in heaven, and come, follow Me." Matthew 19:21 LSB

Andrew Carnegie came to America as a young boy from Scotland in 1848. He worked hard to become a very successful steel baron. But his riches bothered him, and he sold his steel company at the age of 66. He spent the rest of his life giving away money to charitable organizations, many of which he founded. When he died, he had donated $350 million of the $480 million he had received for the sale of his company. We are all impacted by his generosity through public libraries, medical advancements like insulin, and arts and entertainment like Carnegie Hall and Sesame Street. Carnegie used his wealth to benefit others in meaningful ways.

Last week in *A Better Way*, we explored God's better way of meekness and how it makes us strong.

- Becoming meek is not weakness but a choice to submit to God and His strength.
- Love for God and the indwelling of the Holy Spirit are the sources of this strength.
- Jesus modeled meekness for us through His humanity; He has empathy for our weaknesses and struggles.
- Meekly standing still is really a position of power because of God's supremacy.
- The King of Kings wants us to inherit the earth, but the way to rule is to submit to Him.

This week we will look at another aspect of God's upside-down Kingdom: giving away to receive. Our natural tendency to hold on to possessions is a sign that we need to learn how to give like Him. God-generosity is part of following Jesus, the most generous gift ever given.

—— DAY 1: STINKIN' THINKIN'

Father, thank You for providing this time for us to meet together today. I open my heart and mind to whatever You have to tell me as I read and meditate on Your Word.

I love to scrapbook, and several albums contain pages of my grandson's growth over the years. When he looks at the pages with me, he will sometimes point out a toy in a photo and say, "I don't have that anymore." We talk about how things in life come and go, and that is normal and okay. Sometimes he's almost surprised that he had a toy in the past; it's as though it never happened because he was too young to remember it.

Our discussions remind me that possessions are not forever. Since that's true, it's best not to hold on to them too tightly. Jesus taught us that in His Kingdom, property is of little value. This attitude is upside-down from the philosophy of this world. Everywhere we look we are encouraged to buy more, accumulate more, and hoard more. Your worth as a person is measured by the size of your house, the make of your car, and the number who follow you on social media. But Jesus had a different idea about what is most important. Read Matthew 6:19-21. Where did Jesus say to accumulate treasures and why?

_____

_____

_____

In verse 21, what connection did Jesus make between your treasure and your heart?

_____

_____

What does the concept of storing up treasures in heaven look like for you?

_____

_____

For those of us with healthy eating challenges, this better way can be very helpful. Are you storing up food in the pantry that isn't the best choice for you? How could this challenge be addressed with the idea of storing up treasures in heaven? One way might be to let go of these unhealthy food options by leaving them at the store. You can't eat it if it isn't there. As you shop for groceries, think about putting food in your basket that will reflect your efforts to put value on things in heaven rather than on earth.

Jesus said storing things on earth is pointless because these things will rot and decay. Have you ever come across something that has rotted? It is not pleasant, and it usually stinks! If we put our focus on things of this world, whether it's possessions or food, that is "stinkin' thinkin'." Food cannot bring me security, whether here on earth or in heaven. Attempting to use food to fill me in any form except to fuel my body in healthy ways comes from "stinkin' thinkin'," which will result in missed blessings and possible physical and emotional problems.

How do we overcome "stinkin' thinkin'?" Paul has some ideas about this subject. Read Philippians 1:21 and 3:8. What did he consider most valuable?

_____

_____

_____

Let's consider the surpassing value of the Kingdom of God. Although it is upside-down from our society and our own fleshly desires, God's Kingdom is where we find stability and permanence. Look up Matthew 13:44-46. How should we value His Kingdom?

_____

_____

_____

I confess, Lord, that I have problems with "stinkin' thinkin'," putting higher value on earthly things rather than You and Your Kingdom. Give me wisdom and a heavenly perspective when it comes to food and my possessions. I thank You for Your Spirit's work in me to make me more like Jesus. Amen.

—— DAY 2: MONEY LOVING

Holy Lord, I am blessed to meet with You in this quiet time and place, away from the hustle of the day. Speak to my heart and fill me with Your Spirit as I learn more of You.

My mother loved dishes. After her retirement she collected a variety of sets of dishes and used them to entertain family and friends. She even had *three sets* of Christmas dishes! At one time, she had packed her cupboards so full of dishes that the cupboards began to come loose from the wall. They were important to her because they helped her show her love to others by serving them food on lovely plates. But she certainly had more dishes than she needed.

The Kingdom of God is a place of abundance, but not in the way the world values wealth. Jesus knew that our desire for things was an important topic to confront. For example, eleven of Jesus' forty parables were about money, and he often used money to teach principles about values. Read Matthew 6:24 and describe what He said about money.

_____

_____

_____

Read Matthew 19:16-22. What did Jesus challenge the rich young ruler to do?

_____

_____

_____

What was his response?

_____

_____

_____

Why do you think Jesus challenged him in this way?

_____

_____

_____

Jesus went on to say more about money in Matthew 19:23-26. Record His teaching from verses 23-24.

_____

_____

_____

His disciples were aghast at this statement and asked how anyone could be saved (verse 25). What was Jesus' reply in verse 26?

_____

_____

_____

Jesus' disciples, like many people of this time and place, believed that wealth was a sign of God's blessing and poverty was a sign of God's punishment, based on whether or not you were "good enough." Jesus' disciples were not rich, nor did He focus on ministering to the rich. He purposely sought out those on the fringes of society: the Samaritan woman, tax-collectors, lepers, prostitutes, fishermen, and shepherds. He knew that they were less likely to be dependent on their worldly possessions and might be more open to His message of love and grace. Those who were rich and in power, even the religious rulers, trusted in their worldly acquisitions to keep them safe and in control. Jesus' upside-down Kingdom threatened their status quo. So it was more difficult for them to accept Jesus' sacrificial gift of salvation. Jesus often used hyperbole to illustrate His truths. In this case, He created an image of an enormous animal attempting to go through the smallest of spaces. Depending on earthly things instead of God creates a barrier to the blessings of His new birth.

In this story, a rich young ruler came to Jesus and asked what good thing he needed to do to inherit eternal life. Jesus knew his heart and challenged him to keep God's laws. The young man claimed he had kept them all. But Jesus knew that he may have kept the letter of the law but that his heart was set on earthly things, not heavenly things. Write our memory verse for this week, Matthew 19:21, and circle what Jesus said the young man needed to do to gain eternal life.

_____

_____

_____

The rich young ruler went away sad because he couldn't trade his passion for his possessions for a commitment to Christ. What is your relationship to possessions? Someone has said it is okay to have possessions as long as they do not have you. Paul expressed this idea eloquently in 1 Timothy 6:6-10. Read these verses, meditate on them, and write a prayer to God about your own connections to things in your life.

_____

_____

_____

Lord, only You are able to change my heart. I relinquish my desire to have more things and ask You to help me to crave more of You instead. Help me let go of the things I cherish that are barriers to my devotion to You. Amen.

—— DAY 3: TRUSTING GOD, NOT MONEY

God of the universe, I praise You today for Your love and compassion. As we meet together now, open my eyes and my heart to the wonder of You.

I have been laid off twice in my life. The first time I was pregnant with my second child. It was a part-time job, but my income was critical to my family's survival. My last day of work was on a Friday. Of course, I was praying along with all my Christian family and friends. I was an interpreter for the deaf at my church, and a fellow interpreter called me to let me know that she knew a deaf client who needed an interpreter for her college classes. Through a series of God-directed events, I started work on Monday the Friday after I had been laid off. Interpreting was one of the most fulfilling jobs I ever had, and I was able to earn the money we needed.

When God is working in your life, He will direct you where you are to go and provide what you need. What is important is where we place our trust. Whether you are a gazillionaire or someone who is scraping by is not the issue. Depending on money to take care of your needs can get you into trouble. Depending on God to meet your needs never fails. Read Habakkuk 3:17-19. What condition does the author describe in verse 17?

_____

_____

_____

What is the author's attitude about his situation in verse 18?

_____

_____

_____

What does the author say about God in verse 19?

_____

_____

_____

In her podcast *The Bible Recap*, Tara-Leigh Cobble talks about this passage in Habakkuk.

God warns [the Israelites] about putting their hope in wealth, security, power, pleasure, and control. When they pursue each of those things as ultimate, they each lead to unique kinds of sin. Those who look to wealth as their ultimate hope will steal and cheat to get it. Those who look to security will oppress others to protect themselves. Those who look to power will enslave people, kill people, and work themselves to death. Those who look to pleasure will engage in drunkenness and debauchery but will end up in shame instead. Those who look to control will try to grasp it any way they can, even if the source is through idols and false gods. We can probably all see ourselves in those five categories. God calls people to turn their eyes from these false hopes and remember not only that He exists, but to honor Him instead. Habakkuk prays and asks God to show Himself mighty. He knows what God is capable of. He's seen God's works in the past and wants to see those kinds of works again in the present, but resolves to wait for God's timing. He commits to trust God and not object to His process. This is what faith looks like. Faith says, "Nothing is going the way I want it to. Everything is falling apart, but I won't put my hope in wealth, security, power, pleasure, or control because I know they will fail me or even lead my heart away from God. I know that I can be strengthened and fulfilled regardless of my circumstances because fruitful vines and filled stalls aren't where the joy is. He's where the joy is!"[1]

How have you seen God's works in the past?

_____

_____

_____

How do you want to see those kinds of works again in the present?

_____

_____

_____

Do you have the resolve to wait for God's timing? If so, how?

_____

_____

_____

Read Hebrews 11:24-27 and describe Moses' experience.

_____

_____

_____

In verse 26 what did Moses value more than the treasures of Egypt?

_____

_____

In Ecclesiastes 5:10 what happens when we love money and wealth?

_____

_____

_____

The second time I was laid off I was working at one of our state's regional education centers. There was a massive layoff due to funding cuts, and I was the most recently hired in my group. One morning my bosses met with me to let me know I would no longer have a job in a couple of months. Later the same day I went to talk to the director of another department with whom I had been helping with a project. When I told her I would be leaving, she said, "That's fine. Now you can work for me. Would you like to see your office?" I was laid off and employed on the same day! I was once again amazed by God's direction and provision. I actually had two jobs for a few months as I transitioned between departments and made some extra money! In both of my circumstances, I learned that my job was not where I should place my trust. It can obviously disappear in a heartbeat. My faith should be in God, the great Provider, whether He sends a great amount at once or bread just for the day. We can trust Him for what we need, and He will never forsake us or leave us alone. Where does your trust lie: in God or in money? How can you tell?

_____

_____

_____

You are the God Who owns the cattle on a thousand hills. I know I can trust You to provide whatever I need at just the right time. Give me patience as You work to teach me to depend on You alone and not physical wealth. I know that nothing can satisfy me but You. Amen.

—— DAY 4: ACCOUNTABILITY

My soul magnifies You, Lord, for You are great and mighty. May Your words impact my heart today in new ways as I seek You first.

Brett Favre is one of the greatest names in football. The Hall of Fame quarterback earned three consecutive MVP awards and a Super Bowl ring and retired as the all-time leader in passing yardage and touchdowns. But in 2022 he faced a crisis when it was discovered that he, along with the University of Mississippi, defrauded the government out of millions of dollars. He had to pay back a large sum he had received for speeches he didn't give, and his integrity was compromised.

Even if you are famous, wealthy, and respected, there are consequences for your actions. There is nothing beyond God's watchful eyes. What does Job 34:21 say?

_____

_____

_____

One of the most important aspects of our First Place for Health ministry is the accountability that comes with community. You attend a weekly group meeting. You keep a food diary and share it with your leader. You contact a member from your group each week. These practices help us make healthy choices because we know others who care about us will hold us accountable to the program we agreed to follow.

Jesus told a story that truly illustrates the economy of the upside-down Kingdom He was announcing. The people of His time thought that wealth and status meant you were a better person than a person who was poor. They believed prosperity was evidence of God's favor and poverty was a sign of His disfavor. Look up Luke 16:19-21 and describe the situation of the rich man and Lazarus on earth.

_____

_____

_____

Read verses 22-23; where did each man go after he died?

_____

_____

_____

45

In verse 24 what request does the rich man make of Abraham?

_____

_____

_____

What is Abraham's reply (verses 25-26)?

_____

_____

_____

The rich man made a second request in verses 27-28 and 30. What was it?

_____

_____

_____

What was Abraham's reply in verses 29 and 31?

_____

_____

_____

What does this story teach us about accountability?

_____

_____

_____

Our earthly possessions and our desire for them can interfere with our devotion to God and passion for helping others. James denounced the behavior of the rich people in the early church. Read James 5:1-6. What does he say about their condition in verse 5?

_____

_____

_____

James did not condemn the rich people for being rich. He condemned them for not seeking God's Kingdom first with their riches. They used their riches to satisfy themselves rather than help others. In God's upside-down Kingdom, the rich are those who use what they have for His glory not their own comfort and status. Jesus put a spin on this idea in Matthew 25:34-40. What does he say about our charity to others in verse 40?

_____

_____

_____

How do you regard your own money and possessions? Do you use them for yourself alone or to help others? Do your decisions about money reflect a heart that loves God more than self? What accountability practices do you have in place for your use of the resources which God has given you?

_____

_____

_____

You are a good, good God, Father, and You give me abundance beyond my need. I want to be a good steward of all those blessings. Hold me accountable for my food choices as well as the choices I make with everything You entrust to me. I know I have nothing apart from Your divine grace. Amen.

—— DAY 5: A GIVING ATTITUDE

Thank You for giving me a new day to praise and serve You, Lord. You have much to teach me and much for me to do for Your glory. Let me hear You as You speak to me now.

Chad was a shy, quiet boy who was excluded from his elementary school peers' activities. Yet he told his mother he wanted to make a valentine card for each child in his class. He worked hard on the cards and took them to school on February 14th. After school, he came running home, breathlessly crying out, "Not a one!" His mother's heart sunk, thinking her son had given all his handmade cards to his classmates but hadn't received any himself. She greeted him with milk and cookies, hoping to ease his pain. But he repeated, "Not a one! Not a one!" As she tried to calm him down, she noticed his big smile as he cheerfully chirped, "Not a one! I didn't forget a one!"[2]

Chad's attitude about giving is what Jesus taught His disciples. His better way is to give with great joy and without concern for what we get in return. Look up Matthew 6:1-4. What attitude does Jesus encourage in these verses?

_____

_____

_____

Read 2 Corinthians 9:6-7 and describe the attitude Paul instructs concerning giving.

_____

_____

_____

In 1 Corinthians 13:3 we learn the motivation we need to give cheerfully. What is it?

_____

_____

_____

These aspects of a giving attitude in Jesus' Kingdom involve selflessness, cheerfulness, and love. How does this relate to my fitness and wellness journey? Sometimes I'm not very happy about the healthy choices I need to make. I want to eat what I enjoy rather than stick to a sensible food plan. But if I change my way of thinking about my food choices as a way to give sacrificially and cheerfully to the God I love and Who loves me, my attitude can change. When I choose vegetables and fruit over sugary desserts, I can smile and say, "Thank You, God, that You have provided these healthy options that will make my body well and strong." I can relinquish my desires for less healthy food as a gift to God, given freely out of love with a cheerful attitude.

Sometimes we make the right choices but do so with grumbling and resentment. We might think, "Why do I have to make the sacrifice to eat this food while others can eat whatever they want and never gain a pound?" It can be difficult to make the best choices and feel cheerful, but God can change our desires if we continue to seek Him first. I read that someone decided to do something to show God she wanted to eat well and began doing something small to show her commitment to Him over food. At every meal, she left the last bite on her plate. That might not seem like a big deal. But for those of us who struggle with eating issues, especially compulsive overeating, that's huge. She cheerfully and voluntarily gave a bite of food to God, motivated by love for Him.

Read Psalm 119:36; what does the writer ask God to do?

_____

_____

_____

In Matthew 19:29 what does Jesus promise to those who have given up what they cherish for His sake?

_____

_____

_____

God's Word is our true food, and He will give back to us when we give our all to Him. What can you give to God today that would be selfless, cheerful, and loving? How do your food choices reflect giving your life and desires to Him?

_____

_____

_____

I confess, Lord, that I do not always give selflessly, cheerfully, and lovingly. I want my life to reflect the extravagance You have given to me through Jesus. Show me where I can give from my heart to You and to others in need. Amen.

—— DAY 6: REFLECTION AND APPLICATION

My heart yearns for You, Father, for Your peace and comfort. As I pause and remember that You are God, show me more of Your love and power. I need You, Lord.

As we consider what giving away to receive means, let's reflect on the sufficiency of God and His economy. First, God can take whatever we give Him and multiply it. I like the expression, "Little Is Much When God Is in It," the title of a song by Bill Gaither. Whether you're talking about the loaves and fish that fed thousands or daily manna in the wilderness, God excels in taking the little or nothing that we have to offer and enlarging it beyond what we need. How has God multiplied something small to meet your needs?

_____

_____

_____

Second, we can never out-give God. No matter how much we contribute, He will give us more. Jesus put it this way in Luke 6:38: "Give, and it will be given to you. A good measure, pressed down, shaken together and running over, will be poured into your lap. For with the measure you use, it will be measured to you." You will not be able to contain the abundance of God's provisions. In Malachi 3:10 God challenges us to "Bring the whole tithe into the storehouse, that there may be food in my house. 'Test me in this,' says the LORD Almighty, 'and see if I will not throw open the floodgates of heaven and pour out so much blessing that there will not be room enough to store it.'" How has God out-given you?

_____

_____

_____

Finally, our need to give is greater than God's need for what we give Him. Since He owns the cattle on a thousand hillsides (Psalm 50:10), He really doesn't need what I have. Actually, what I have is His anyway because James 1:17 says "Every good and perfect gift is from above." Jesus says it is more blessed to give than receive (Acts 20:35). Giving is an opportunity to worship and praise God, because giving demonstrates my thanksgiving to Him for providing for me. And it and shows my love for others. How has God blessed you when you gave?

_____

_____

_____

Certainly, the best example of giving away to receive is God's gift of His only Son Jesus to redeem us to Himself. As we practice giving, let's remember that supreme act of love and may it compel us to relinquish our desires for earthly possessions and develop a passion for eternal priorities. How will you practice giving this week?

_____

_____

_____

I cannot grasp the enormity of Your acts of generosity and love, Lord. You fill my life with more than I can contain and You encourage me to give as You have given to me. Show me today how I can practice giving away to receive, and motivate me with Your love that sacrificed Your best for me. I love You. Amen.

—— DAY 7: REFLECTION AND APPLICATION

In Your presence I find all I need, Father. You fill me with Your goodness and cleanse me from my sins. Guide my thoughts now as I draw aside from my busyness to focus on You.

Practice this week's memory verse here:

_____

_____

_____

This week's study on God's better way of giving away to receive has challenged us to view our earthly possessions in a different perspective. The paradox of giving away some yet receiving more is an essential part of Jesus' upside-down Kingdom. As you reflect and journal about what God has revealed to you, ask Him to show you how this practice can begin or increase in your life. Here are some prompts from which you may choose for your journaling and reflection.

• Create a two-column chart; title one column "Stinkin' Thinkin'" and the other column "The Mind of Christ." Under the first column list things that represent storing up your treasures on earth, and under the second column list things that represent storing up your treasure in heaven. You can include images if you wish.

• Draw a large circle. Divide the circle into sections like a pie chart with each section representing an area where you spend your money. For example, one section would be rent or house payment, another would be food, and another would be money spent on car and gas. What does this graph tell you about how you spend your money? How does God fit into your decisions about your budget and expenses?

• Recall a time when you faced a financial crisis. How did God work in that situation? How did you trust Him for providing for your needs? What did you learn about Him and His faithfulness?

• Take a picture of your closet or pantry. Put a copy of the picture in your journal and write about the abundance God has given you. How will you give from what He has provided to help others?

• Find a song that encourages you in this process. You may document the lyrics and record your own reflections on them, or you could illustrate them with sketches or images you locate. Two examples for this week's study are "Give Me Your Eyes" by Brandon Heath (2008) and "Give It Away" by Gloria and Benjamin Gaither (2006).

Your journal is a very private and personal process; therefore, share it carefully. If social media is a healthy place for you, use these hashtags for posting your words, images, other reflections, or personal stories from this study: #fp4h and #fp4habetterway. You can view my journal and others' entries using these hashtags.

Everything I have is Yours, Father. I give it all back to You cheerfully and ask You to help me have the same attitude as Yours when it comes to giving. May everything I do and say be a reflection of Your generous gift of Jesus, Who is my all in all. Amen.

1 Tara-Leigh Cobble, "Episode 218"," The Bible Recap Podcast, D-Group (2022), https://www.thebiblerecap.com/.

2 Adapted from "Not A One" by Dale Galloway. Source unknown.

WEEK FOUR: BE HUNGRY TO BECOME SATISFIED

SCRIPTURE MEMORY VERSE

Blessed are those who hunger and thirst for righteousness, for they will be filled.
Matthew 5:6

Willy Wonka & the Chocolate Factory is a beloved movie from 1971. It is based on a Roald Dahl book, *Charlie and the Chocolate Factory*. The five winners of golden tickets hidden inside Wonka candy bars get a tour of the factory and a lifetime supply of chocolate. Four of the children who take the tour are depicted as gluttonous, greedy, and egotistical. They are sent away from the factory one by one because of their obsession with food and demanding ways. Only Charlie remains at the end of the movie because he has exhibited selflessness and respect for Willy Wonka and his confectionary enterprise. As a result Willy Wonka plans to give the factory to Charlie upon his retirement.

Our physical appetites can get in the way of making healthy choices and putting God first. We also have spiritual, emotional, and mental appetites. Trying to satisfy these hungers with food is futile. We can attempt to appease our appetites in other ways: immediate gratification, success and status, or compulsive behaviors to name a few. We may allow ourselves to have whatever we want, whenever we want, thinking that this behavior will bring satisfaction. However, we will find that these things cannot satisfy the inner yearning we have to know God intimately.

Last week in *A Better Way*, we learned about giving to receive.

- Storing up temporary treasures on earth is "stinkin' thinkin'" because only treasure in heaven is eternal.
- Our possessions and money can get in the way of being totally committed to God.
- Our security is in God alone, not our jobs or money. He is the Great Provider.
- We are accountable for our choices and uses of the resources God has entrusted to us.
- Our giving attitude in Jesus' Kingdom involves selflessness, cheerfulness, and love.

This week we will consider another one of Jesus' audacious teachings about His upside-down Kingdom: we become satisfied through our hunger and thirst for righteousness. Paradoxically, true satisfaction for our deepest hungers is found in Him alone as He develops selflessness and respect for Him in our hearts.

—— DAY 1: HUNGERING FOR RIGHTEOUSNESS

I come to you now, Lord, with great anticipation for every time I meet with You, I come away changed in some way. Move in my being and make me more like Jesus.

Matthew 5:3-12 records what we call the Beatitudes. In this passage, Jesus did not describe eight separate groups of people but rather eight characteristics of individuals who follow and seek Him first. They include awareness of their spiritual bankruptcy without God, grief over sin, humility, and desire for right relationships with God and others. Disciples of Jesus exhibit mercifulness, a transparent longing to serve God alone, an eagerness to share the gospel and the peace it gives, and a heavenly perspective of earthly persecution for His sake. These selfless attributes of Christians are upside-down from the selfish ideas about success and satisfaction celebrated by the world and a better way to live.

One of the beatitudes is the focus of this week's study. Write this week's memory verse here.

_____

_____

_____

What does it mean to hunger and thirst after righteousness? First, we must understand what the word righteousness means. What is your current understanding of this word?

_____

_____

_____

Our dictionaries include ideas of right, moral behavior. Let's see what the Bible says about God's ideas of righteousness. The first instance of this idea is in Genesis 15:6. How did Abram attain righteousness?

_____

_____

_____

Righteousness is less about evaluating my behavior and more about developing a faithful relationship with God. That kind of righteousness can produce right, moral behavior. But righteousness itself is born in my dependence on God and faith in His Word. Jesus condemned religious leaders who practiced self-righteousness. Their religious behavior was impeccable, but they had no honest relationship with God or concern for others. Their faith was in themselves, not Him. Read Matthew 23:27-28 and record Jesus' criticism of the Pharisees and scribes.

_____

_____

_____

What does it mean to hunger and thirst after this kind of righteousness? One writer says, "Those who have realized their spiritual bankruptcy mourn their sin in deep anguish. In that deep anguish they realize that their only hope is to turn to Christ. In that state of humility, mourning, and meekness, they have a passion to rid themselves of the sin that fills them and to be filled with what they see in Christ. The Greek word used here expresses a passionate longing for something without which one cannot live."[1] That passion to be filled with Christ is a hunger and thirst for righteousness.

How does Paul express this well in Philippians 3:7-11?

_____

_____

_____

Saint Augustine wrote in *Confessions of a Sinner*, "You have made us for yourself, O Lord, and our hearts are restless until they rest in You" (AD 397-400).[2] A restless heart is a divine gift. The world tells us to seek satisfaction in whatever way we can find it. A Christian's restless heart for God compels her to constantly seek God first and love Him more in all things.

Each Beatitude starts with the word *blessed*. *Blessed* has the idea of being enlarged. We are enlarged by God through His blessings when we hunger and thirst after righteousness. He fills us and satisfies us as only He can. Our memory verse, Matthew 5:6, reads like this in The Message: "You're blessed when you've worked up a good appetite for God. He's food and drink in the best meal you'll ever eat."

How are you hungry and thirsty for God's righteousness?

_____

_____

_____

Thank You for providing righteousness for me through faith in Jesus. I am blessed by Your generous gift. Give me a passionate hunger and thirst for relationship with You, my Lord. Only You can satisfy me in the deepest places of my being. Amen.

—— DAY 2: PHYSICAL VERSUS SPIRITUAL HUNGER

I am thankful today, dear Father, that You are my refuge. Give attention to me as I seek Your face while I praise You for Your mighty power and love.

In the First Place for Health program, we practice several spiritual disciplines. They include daily prayer, Bible reading, Bible study, and scripture memorization. Why would we do these things in order to lose weight, exercise our bodies, and make healthy choices? What is the connection between taking care of our bodies and hungering for righteousness?

When we are physically hungry, we have an empty place to fill with food. Spiritual hunger means we have an empty place inside that only God can fill. Psalm 42:1-2 describes this hunger well; read the verses and restate them in your own words.

_____

_____

_____

The deer would pant for flowing streams because it is thirsty. We pant for God because only He can satisfy the spiritual thirst within us. In Isaiah 55:1-2 what is the invitation that God gives to us?

_____

_____

_____

What would my life look like as though I hungered for God as much as or more than I hunger for food? Hungering for God starts with changing from the inside out, the transformative power of the Holy Spirit in our lives to direct our desires on a Christian course. Read John 6:35. Why do you think Jesus used the imagery of bread to identify Himself?

_____

_____

_____

We may satisfy our needs for physical pleasure but ignore our spiritual needs. We can become bloated with worldly things and have less room for God. I must be empty to become filled, and trying to satisfy spiritual hunger with physical things can keep me from finding true satisfaction. Stop and ask yourself before you eat: Is this what I'm really hungry for? I daresay that I am rarely really physically hungry. However, I can be tempted to eat when what I really want is God. I want to experience Him. I want Him to answer a need for which I've earnestly prayed. I want to understand His truths and dig deeper into His Word. Food cannot satisfy those desires. When my spirit is growling like a hungry stomach, I need to come to Him for nourishment. Find Psalm 63:1 and describe the psalmist's condition.

_____

_____

_____

An interesting phenomenon occurs when we seek God to satisfy our spiritual hunger. We are sated yet our craving is increased. It's like eating potato chips; they are good but you always want one more. God is sweet and satisfying, but He is endlessly desirable. So hungering and thirsting after righteousness is a _continual_ state of following Jesus and becoming more like Him. This is also called _sanctification_, the continual process of growing into the person God created you to be, an image and reflection of Him with an eternal purpose. We are hungry to be filled by Him, and that filling results in growth.

Our four-sided beings need to be fed in all four areas: emotional, spiritual, mental, and physical. When we try to satisfy the needs of the first three with something physical, like food, the hunger remains and may intensify. Identifying what we are truly hungry for and satisfying that hunger appropriately is a key to managing our physical health, as well as our overall well-being. How could practicing spiritual disciplines help you make healthy food choices?

_____

_____

_____

You alone are my source of satisfaction, Lord. When I am hungry for You, help me recognize that desire and keep me from using food as a substitute for filling me spiritually. Help me be intentional in practicing spiritual disciplines that bring me closer to You. Amen.

── DAY 3: PHYSICAL VERSUS MENTAL HUNGER

Father, today is a new day for loving and serving You. I know You are with me every moment, and I'm thankful for this quiet time to share my heart with You.

I taught students and their teachers for 35 years. One thing I learned from this experience is that curiosity is a natural human characteristic. Young children are full of questions and eager to get answers to them. But for many reasons, classroom education can stunt that curious excitement. Teachers ask the questions, and students give the answers. By the time students ended up in my middle school classroom, they didn't know how nor want to ask questions any more. I felt like they were thinking, "Just give me the answer and don't make me think." I worked with them to reignite that curious enthusiasm and taught them how to ask questions again.

Curiosity is a mental activity. Our minds are amazing organs, designed by God to make us unique among all His creation. And it is in our minds that our hunger and thirst for righteousness is developed. Thoughts about God and our relationship to Him affect our emotions and actions. And feeding our minds is just as important as feeding our spirits and bodies. How can we feed our minds in healthy ways? First, our minds need to be fed the Word of God. Read the verses below and record what they say about the impact of God's Word on our minds. Note: The idea about thinking in the brain was not fully understood during Biblical times. The word "heart" can refer to the place where thinking takes place as well as the word "mind."

Scripture	How God's Word Impacts Our Minds
Psalm 40:8	
Colossians 3:16	
2 Timothy 3:16-17	

When we engage with God's Word daily, it changes our thinking and attitudes. We are challenged in First Place for Health to read the Bible daily so that we read it through in a year's time. This task is not easy, but the rewards are enormous. Meditating on His Word cultivates a God-centered view of life, a real game-changer. How do you feed your mind with God's Word, and how does it impact your thinking?

_____

_____

_____

Second, our minds need a balance of stimulus and rest. Both boredom and exhaustion can influence us to make unhealthy choices. We can counteract these extremes by intentionally scheduling time to rest and time to be active. Let's see what God has to say about rest. Read Matthew 11:28-30 and summarize what Jesus offers us.

_____

_____

_____

How does Hebrews 4:9-10 emphasize our need for rest?

_____

_____

_____

Sometimes the most spiritual thing we can do is take a nap! Giving our mind daily down time allows it to refresh itself and process the multitude of input it has received. That rest should be balanced with healthy stimuli for us to:

- Learn new things.
- Read a variety of books that expand our thoughts and challenge our thinking.
- Participate in a hobby that gives us pleasure and opportunities to solve problems.
- Go to the gym or for a walk, because exercise helps our brains.
- Listen to music or podcasts that encourage and teach us.
- Get involved in organizations or activities that help other people.

Third, our minds need healthy content. We should consider what kinds of things we feed our mind. Television, videos, podcasts, and social media are not inherently bad, but we must evaluate the content available and choose wisely. Limiting time on social media that overwhelms or discourages us is wise.

What criteria does Philippians 4:8 give us to judge the content we feed our minds?

_____

_____

_____

Our thinking impacts our healthy choices, and we can choose how we think about food. God can help us develop a hunger and thirst for righteousness that can replace our food-obsessed thinking. Record your responses to these questions.

- When are you most tempted to make an unhealthy food choice?
- Do you think about food constantly?
- Do you think you should eat just because it is a certain time of day?
- Are you thinking about eating to avoid something?
- Do you think you should eat because you are attending an event?

_____

_____

_____

_____

_____

_____

What does God-centered thinking look like as opposed to food-centered thinking? Jesus certainly modeled this upside-down Kingdom behavior in many ways. In Matthew 4:4 He said we don't live by bread alone but by God's Word. In John 4:34 He said His food was to do the will of the Father. Thinking about God's Word and being involved in doing His will feeds our minds in healthy ways so we are more likely to make healthy choices.

What is something you can do today to feed your mind in a positive way?

_____

_____

_____

My Lord, my mind can become easily distracted, overwhelmed, or bored, and that can cause me to make poor food choices. Give me the mind of Christ, which hungers and thirsts for You more than food. Take every one of my thoughts captive under the authority of Jesus so I will follow Your best paths for me. Amen.

—— DAY 4: PHYSICAL VERSUS EMOTIONAL HUNGER

My heart aches to know You more, Father. I have empty places only You can fill. Fill me with all You are as I bow and study Your Word.

As I have sought wellness for over forty years through First Place for Health, I am constantly faced with the reality of emotional eating. Emotional hunger is relentless and intense. Today we will explore what causes emotional hunger and how can we engage with God to combat the urge to eat our feelings.

We have emotional connections to food based on our experiences. If we associate a certain food or eating with a pleasurable memory, it feels comforting to eat when we are hurting inside. But often that eating episode is followed by guilt and shame, which adds to the emotional hunger we feel we must feed. God's Word can give us some answers to this dilemma. The Psalms are full of expressions of intense emotions. Turn to Psalm 61:1-3. How does David share his feelings with God?

_____

_____

_____

There are three steps we can practice to manage emotional eating. First, we can express our feelings to God. He is ready and eager to listen to the pleas of our hearts, to live in the pain with us. One of the things that drives emotional hunger is isolating and hiding feelings. Opening our hearts to God is a first step to stopping the cycle of emotional eating. The feelings may be easy or difficult to name, but until you feel your feelings and open them up to God, they will remain secret and hungry. What is concealed can control us; what is revealed can redeem us.

Second, we can process our feelings with God. As you read Philippians 4:6-7, list the things Paul tells us to do with our feelings.

1. Do not be _____ about anything.
2. In every _____ by _____
3. And _____
4. With_____
5. Present your _____ to _____

What are the two results?

1. The _____of_____, which transcends all _____
2. Will _____ your _____ and _____ in _____

_____

Paul begins with "do not be anxious." Then he explains how to deal with anxiety: we put it before God in faith. We pray about every situation, good and bad, all the time, constantly. Even when we don't know the outcome of the situation we face, we do know the One Who will be with us in the midst of it all and carry us to other side.

Finally, we can *reprogram* our responses to our feelings. Feelings come from the way we think and perceive our world. If someone does something that hurts me, I can choose how I respond. I could go to one extreme or another: lash out in anger or quietly stew over the hurt. Either of these choices will likely result in some unwanted consequences. Or I can go to God's Word and let Him speak to me about how I respond. Look up 2 Corinthians 10:5 and record how we can change our thinking.

_____

_____

_____

Yesterday we looked at the impact of the Bible on our thinking. Continuing to feed our mind with God's Word will impact our feelings as well. One study has found that being involved with the Bible influences us "practically, emotionally, and missionally. When Scripture is a driving force in a person's life, that person is influenced mind, body, and soul by the Word of God—'built on the Bible...'"[3]

If you have ever experienced a panic attack, you may feel these words are trite and ineffective. I have had panic attacks. They are frightening and confusing. Focusing on prayer, scripture, music, and tangible things in my surroundings helped me in the midst of the attack. Once I'm on the other side, I can work with God to help me process the feelings that contributed to the panic. I've sought the help of a counselor and learned other techniques for dealing with this overwhelming physical response to emotional pain.

Writer and podcaster Barb Raveling says, "What usually happens when you take the time to work through the emotion is that your desire to eat will disappear. If you don't take the time, that emotion has to go somewhere. Usually, it goes to the kitchen looking for something to eat."[4] Hungering and thirsting after righteousness include seeking God's help when things aren't right, when we suffer injustice and are wounded by the world. Do you have a hurt that needs healing? What is something you will do this week to address this wound and take it God rather than food?

_____

_____

_____

Father, my feelings are real. I lay them before You, trusting You for healing and peace. I know You love me and want to hold me closely in Your arms of comfort. Keep me safe in your embrace. Amen.

—— DAY 5: EMPTY TO BECOME FULL

What a privilege to meet with You, Father, to lay open my heart and receive Your Word. Nourish my soul in this quiet time together.

Many people are blessed to live today without ever knowing true hunger. But groups of people all over the world, even in America, do not have enough to eat every day. Malnutrition continues to plague humanity, even in an age of advanced technology and seeming plenty. Deep pangs of physical hunger can be devastating and relentless.

What causes hunger? We have an empty stomach that craves food. We need food to survive. What causes hunger and thirst for righteousness? We have emptiness in our spirit that craves God's sustenance. We cannot be hungry if we are already full. We must empty our lives of things that keep us from desiring God's righteousness.

Peter experienced this idea of being empty to become full. Read Luke 5:1-11 and put yourself in Peter's sandals. What did he tell Jesus in verse 5?

_____

_____

_____

What was the result of following Jesus' advice (verse 6-7)?

_____

_____

Empty nets were required for Jesus to show Peter how Jesus could fill them. If his nets had been full from his own efforts, there would have been no room for Jesus' miracle. How can we empty ourselves so we have room for His filling?

This week we've looked at hunger in all four parts of our beings: physical, spiritual, mental, and emotional. Each of those parts can be emptied so that God can fill them. Look up the following passages and identify how they tell us to become empty.

Parts of Our Beings: Scripture	How to Become Empty
Physical: Matthew 6:16-18	
Spiritual: Matthew 6:33	
Mental: Ephesians 4:22-24	
Emotional: Ephesians 4:31	

What are some practical ways we can empty ourselves?

- **Physical:** Fasting is a practice that can pull our focus away from physical things and sharpen our sensitivity to God. We can fast from many different things: food, shopping, technology, and talking. Putting God before something that has our affection is a powerful way to empty ourselves so He can fill us.
- **Spiritual:** Confession of sin is a first step to seeking God first and emptying ourselves of pride. We can ask God to show us where we are not obeying Him completely, talk to Him about our struggle to agree with Him about our sin, and rejoice in the forgiveness He freely gives. A clean heart is ready to receive the King and His blessings.
- **Mental:** We can remove mental distractions by cutting back on screen time. When things constantly nag our mind, we can put them on a list and set them aside while we think about God and His Word. Creating a gratitude journal helps us focus His blessings rather than ruminate on the things that worry us.
- **Emotional:** For me, journaling is my greatest tool in managing my emotional health. Getting something down on paper seems to help release it from my inner being. Talking with a close friend or counselor about our emotional burdens can also help lighten the load and free up emotional space for God to fill.

You've heard the expression, "She's so full of herself." We certainly can be so consumed by our own agendas, selfish desires, and unhealed pain that there is no room for God to fill us. Daily practices in all four areas of our beings can give us space for God's sufficiency. What is something you can do this week to empty yourself?

_____

_____

_____

Look up Psalm 107:8-9 and write it here.

_____

_____

_____

I thank You, Lord, for Your abundance and Your desire to fill me to overflowing. Help me identify areas in my life that I have crammed full with things that prevent me from experiencing Your fullness. I want to hunger and thirst after Your righteousness. Amen.

—— DAY 6: REFLECTION AND APPLICATION

Hello, Father, I'm here to listen to You. I know that without Your Word and Your Spirit, I can do nothing. Speak to my waiting heart and change me.

To the world, a righteous person seems odd, a misfit. Hungering and thirsting after God is in opposition to the world's systems and values. The world tells us to do everything we can to satisfy our hungers: eat this and you will feel better, use this toothpaste and your love life will be fantastic, and drive this car so everyone will like you. These are lies that distract us from the truth of God's Word: being hungry is good, and being hungrier for God is better.

If I want to develop a hunger and thirst for God's righteousness, one thing I must do is empty myself. Then God can fill me with Himself. There is no hunger if I have already filled myself with things of this world. Read Proverbs 21:21; what are the benefits of pursuing righteousness?

_____

_____

_____

I've found that one thing I must empty to experience God's filling is my expectations. I began following Jesus at a young age, and I developed the idea that He would keep me from experiencing pain if I obeyed Him. I wanted to use Him as a shield against suffering. But nowhere in God's Word does He promise me freedom from sorrow if I follow Him. In fact, He says just the opposite. What does Jesus direct His potential disciples to do in Luke 14:27?

_____

_____

_____

Read the following words and write your reflections about them.

"Cheap grace is the preaching of forgiveness without requiring repentance, baptism without church discipline. Communion without confession. Cheap grace is grace without discipleship, grace without the cross, grace without Jesus Christ, living and incarnate...costly grace confronts us as a gracious call to follow Jesus, it comes as a word of forgiveness to the broken spirit and the contrite heart. It is costly because it compels a man to submit to the yoke of Christ and follow him; it is grace because Jesus says: 'My yoke is easy and my burden is light.'"[5]

These words were written by Dietrich Bonhoeffer, a German theologian and writer, in his book, *The Cost of Discipleship*, originally published in 1937. He lived during the rise of the Nazi party and spoke out against its regime. He was arrested in 1943 and eventually sent to a concentration camp. He was hanged in April 1945, only one month before the end of World War II in Europe. He paid the ultimate price for following Jesus. He didn't let the threat of persecution keep him from speaking the truth. His life is an example and inspiration to us, showing us how to hunger and thirst for righteousness regardless of the consequences, to empty ourselves and be filled with God.

John Wesley was another person who modeled a life that seeks God's righteousness. He wrote the following prayer around 1780 to express a renewal of our covenant with God in Christ. It expresses the desire to be thoroughly consumed by God, to follow Him completely and without any reservation. Let's pray it today to end our quiet time with God and His Word. Meditate on how you can be empty so God can keep you hungry for Him.

I am no longer my own but yours. Put me to what you will, rank me with whom you will. Put me to doing, put me to suffering. Let me be employed for you or laid aside for you, exalted for you or brought low for you. Let me be full, let me be empty. Let me have all things, let me have nothing. I freely and wholeheartedly yield all things to your pleasure and disposal. And now, glorious and blessed God, Father, Son, and Holy Spirit, you are mine and I am yours. So be it. And the covenant now made on earth, let it be ratified in heaven. Amen.[6]

Holy Lord, I am Yours. Take away my selfish expectations, my desires for comfort, and my earth-bound focus. Empty me so I can be filled with only You. Give me a deeper hunger and thirst for Your righteousness as I seek You first. Amen.

—— DAY 7: REFLECTION AND APPLICATION

I bring my needs to You today, Lord. I am weak but You are strong. I am limited but You are limitless. Fill every corner of my being as I bow before You now.

This week we have explored God's better way of becoming satisfied by continually hungering and thirsting after Him and His righteousness. Our ideas of self-righteousness have been challenged, and God's Word has spoken to us about emptying ourselves to be filled with Him. As you spend time reflecting today, may He increase your hunger for Him and give you insight into how He can fill you more. Here are some suggested prompts for journaling or meditating.

- Take a look at your food diary over the past few weeks. How have you chosen to satisfy physical hunger? Consider tracking hunger as opposed to tracking food intake. When are you hungry or think you are hungry? When you are hungry, what do you do to attempt to satisfy your hunger? Try this practice for a week and see what you learn about your need for food versus your need for God.

- Consider what you need to empty from your life. Then think about how God could fill you if you emptied yourself of those things. You can record these as a two-column chart or sketch one cup pouring out the words associated with what you can empty from yourself and a second cup being filled with the words associated with God's filling.

- Write the word *Physical* at the top of the page. Draw three lines from this word to three spaces for lists. Title each list with one of these words: *Spiritual, Mental,* and *Emotional.* List under each of the words the things that cause hunger in that part of your being.

- Find a song that encourages you in this process. You may document the lyrics and record your own reflections on them, or you could illustrate them with sketches or images you locate. Two examples for this week's study are "We Are Hungry" by Bradley Gordon Kilman (2011) and "Hungry (Falling on My Knees)" by Kathryn Scott (2014).

Your journal is a very private and personal process; therefore, share it carefully. If social media is a healthy place for you, use these hashtags for posting your words, images, other reflections, or personal stories from this study: #fp4h and #fp4habetterway. You can view my journal and others' entries using these hashtags.

I am empty apart from Your filling, Lord. Show me the areas in my life where I am substituting Your best for my selfish desires. Heal my brokenness so I can receive all the wonderful things You have planned for me. Restore my life through Your powerful forgiveness and amazing love. Amen.

_____

_____

_____

_____

_____

_____

_____

_____

_____

_____

_____

_____

_____

_____

_____

_____

_____

_____

_____

1 Mike Hamilton, "Those Who Hunger and Thirst after Righteousness," Sermon Central (2003), https://www.sermoncentral.com/sermons/those-who-hunger-and-thirst-for-righteousness-mike-hamilton-sermon-on-growth-in-christ-62851.

2 Saint Augustine, Confessions, trans. Henry Chadwick (Oxford: Oxford University Press, 2008), 3.

3 Renée Griffith, "The Power of Bible Engagement," Bible Engagement Project (2022), https://bibleengagementproject.com/en/Blog/Why-It-Matters/The-Power-of-Bible-Engagement?ref=tfrecipes.

4 Barb Raveling, "28: Help for Emotional Eating: Bible Verses & Questions," Barb Raveling (2016), https://barbraveling.com/emotional-eating/.

5 Dietrich Bonhoeffer, The Cost of Discipleship (New York: Simon and Schuster, 2012), 45.

6 John Wesley, The United Methodist Hymnal (Nashville: Abingdon Press, 1989), Number 607.

WEEK FIVE: SERVE TO BE HONORED

SCRIPTURE MEMORY VERSE
Whoever wants to become great among you must be your servant, and whoever wants to be first must be your slave—just as the Son of Man did not come to be served, but to serve, and to give his life as a ransom for many. Matthew 20:26-28

In the early 1900s a photographer named Lewis Hines took pictures of children who worked in factories and other businesses in America. Children were valued as workers because their small hands could work more easily than adult's hands in the intricate machinery. But they were paid little, worked long hours, and often suffered injuries without compensation. Through Hines' work, along with other reformers' efforts, child labor laws were eventually passed that protected children from this exploitation.

The business owners used children to line their own pockets. They wanted to be great on the backs of others' hard work. There were those same kind of people in Jesus' time, and He spoke out against this worldly mindset. In His upside-down Kingdom, "the last shall be first, and the first shall be last" (Matthew 20:16).

Last week in *A Better Way*, we explored hungering and thirsting for righteousness.
*   Hungering and thirsting after righteousness means having a passion for a faithful relationship with God.
*   Hungering for God starts with changing from the inside out through the transformative power of the Holy Spirit in our lives to direct our desires in a Christian course.
*   When you engage with God's Word daily, it changes your thinking and attitudes.
*   Instead of emotional eating, you can express your feelings to God, process them, and reprogram your responses to your feelings.
*   We must be empty of worldly things to be completely filled with God.

This week we will explore servanthood and how that lifestyle is representative of Jesus' life and calling. We can lose our natural tendencies to promote ourselves and learn God's better way of focusing on others and their needs for His glory.

—— DAY 1: WHAT IS GREATNESS IN GOD'S KINGDOM?

My God, You are my God and I earnestly seek You. You are my life and my breath, my food and my drink. Saturate me now in Your presence.

The Jews of Jesus' time were waiting for a Messiah, a promised King who would come and deliver them. Their expectation was that he would be a military and political conqueror, someone who would free them from Roman oppression. Jesus didn't fit the image of the ruler they sought. His life was much more about leading through serving and modeling love and care for others.

Jesus showed us throughout His brief life how a servant becomes great in the Kingdom of God. When we wonder what greatness looks like, we can observe Him. Let's explore some passages of Scripture that illustrate this servant mindset and practice. Our memory verse comes from Matthew 20:20-28. The mother of James and John, two of Jesus' disciples, came to Jesus, asking Him to allow her sons to sit on His right and left hand when He came into His Kingdom. In verse 23 what was Jesus' comment to James and John?

_____

_____

_____

How did the other disciples react to the mother's request? (verse 24)

_____

_____

Jesus used this moment to teach His disciples about greatness. They believed greatness was being above other people, receiving attention for success, and being praised for their exalted status. That is how greatness was modeled to them by the Jewish leaders. How does Jesus describe this behavior in verse 25?

_____

_____

_____

Jesus then tells His disciples what true greatness looks like. Write this week's memory verses, Matthew 20:26-28, here.

_____

_____

_____

Imagine how the disciples reacted to this radical idea: you serve to *become great*. This concept was the exact opposite of how the Jewish leaders lived. It was against human nature. It was likely not what they signed up for when they chose to follow Jesus. They may have thought some of the glory of the Messiah would rub off on them. But that's not what Jesus taught or modeled for them. God's better way was to focus on sacrificial servanthood, not personal profit.

Even the greatness we may gain from servanthood is not about what we accomplish. Our works for God are only great because He is in it. Only through the work of the Holy Spirit in our lives do we learn to make healthy choices. And one of the healthiest choices we can make is to humbly serve God through ministering to others, just as Jesus did, with humility and an obedient heart.

How important is service in God's Kingdom? The word serve appears over three hundred times in His Word. Jesus said His mission was to "seek and save the lost." (Luke 19:10 ESV) His mission and motivation was not to become great, yet through His servant walk He attained greatness. He calls us to the same lifestyle. We do not seek to become fit and thin in order to be praised for our exceptional excellence and better body. We seek fitness so we can serve Him as long and as well as we can. How does this concept of servanthood impact your desire to make healthy choices with food and exercise?

_____

_____

_____

Holy Father, You are the great God of the universe, yet You sent Your Son Jesus as a servant to this world to show us how greatness comes from serving. His humble and obedient attitude is a challenging model to me, and with Your help I am learning how to serve as He did. Show me how to walk in His steps today as I seek You first. Amen.

—— DAY 2: WHAT DOES A SERVANT'S HEART LOOK LIKE?

Thank You for this quiet time today, Father, when I can halt my hurriedness and find peace in Your presence. Give me understanding and insight as I open Your Word and seek Your face.

God desires that we have a servant mindset as we follow Jesus. What does a servant's heart look like? One of the best examples comes from Jesus Himself on His final night as a human on earth. Turn to John 13 and read verses 1-17. Record the following details about this event.

When: _____

Where: _____

What Jesus did: _____

What Peter said and Jesus' response: _____
_____

What Jesus said (verses 14-15): _____
_____

Some additional context for this scene is found is other gospel accounts. In Mark 14 we learn Jesus and His disciples were in an upper room in Jerusalem. Matthew 20:24 tells us that the disciples were arguing about which of them was the greatest. Jesus knew this would be His last meal with His disciples before His crucifixion. His humanity must have been grieved, and He may have craved sweet fellowship with them for the last time. He had spent the previous week triumphantly entering Jerusalem on a donkey, confronting the Jewish leaders, and being anointed for His death and burial. Now He was alone with His disciples. But no one had taken responsibility to wash their feet, a common practice before a meal, since they walked about in sandals on dusty roads. When He needed His disciples to selflessly serve Him, they failed Him. He knew that eventually they would all desert Him to face torture and death alone. Yet He put His personal needs aside and silently stooped to wash their feet, one of the lowliest jobs He could have done. And He finished this service to them with a final principle: "Very truly I tell you, no servant is greater than his master, nor is a messenger greater than the one who sent him" (John 13:16). This is what a servant's heart looks like: putting aside my own needs to serve others, understanding that I am not above any task that will benefit others. Jesus went on to say in verse 17 that we are blessed when we do these acts of service for others.

Jesus pointed out another person who exhibited a servant's heart in Luke 21:1-4. What happened in these verses?

_____
_____
_____

Here we learn that a servant's heart is *sacrificial*. The widow held nothing back, and Jesus praised her for this seemingly small offering because it represented her willingness to give her all.

Next let's look at an Old Testament example in 1 Chronicles 28. King David was planning for the building of the temple, and part of that plan was to prepare the heart of Solomon, the future King. In the first part of verse 9, with what does David tell Solomon he must serve God?

_____

_____

_____

A servant's heart is also *devoted*. The phrase used here means "a whole (Hebrew *shalem*) heart and a willing mind," the idea that all of the person's being is at peace with a burning desire to serve God and others.

Finally, in Matthew 18:3-5 Jesus gives us an additional insight into a servant's heart. What instructions does He give in these verses?

_____

_____

_____

We learn a third teaching here: a servant's heart is *humble*. Unlike our current culture, children were on the lowest rung of society in Jesus' day. He wants us to welcome people who have been marginalized, shunned, despised, and outcast. A servant's heart doesn't put people in a hierarchy and value some more than others. When a person has a need, a servant looks at the need and serves, regardless of who has the need.

So some of the characteristics of a servant's heart are sacrifice, devotion, and humility. Which of these characteristics best represent your servant's heart?

_____

_____

Which of these characteristics would you like to develop more?

_____

_____

_____

Holy Father, You know my heart better than I know it. You know where I am focused on serving and where I need to develop that attitude. Use Your Holy Spirit to increase my servant mindset and give me opportunities to practice these characteristics as I follow You with all I am. Amen.

—— DAY 3: WHOM DO I SERVE?

My day is not complete without this sacred time with You, my Lord. Quietly now I bow before You, my King, and I listen for Your tender voice of love and instruction.

Australian pastor Noel Atkinson tells a story about the Christian service organization Drum Arm which ministers to drug addicts and sex workers. One of those who received some donuts and coffee wanted to know about this group's motivation. "I know why the government workers are here, I know why the police are here, but why are you guys here?"

Atkinson replied, "Actually I don't like being here, it is dirty and smelly, but I am a Jesus freak and I am here."[1]

Serving others can be dirty, smelly, and uncomfortable. But it is part of membership in God's Kingdom. But whom are we to serve? The Bible teaches that our service should be directed to at least three different groups. The first group is other Christians. Read John 13:34-35. What does Jesus say in verse 34?

_____

_____

_____

What will be the result? (verse 35)

_____

_____

How does 1 John 3:17-18 describe serving other Christians?

_____

_____

_____

The second group of people we are to serve are *those in need*. Jesus told a parable in Matthew 25:31-46 about this group. What needs does He list in verses 35-36?

_____

_____

_____

The people responded to His words with confusion. How did they do these things for Jesus? He was not the one they served. What was Jesus' reply in verse 40?

_____

_____

_____

James 1:27 sums up our practices in serving others. What does this verse say?

_____

_____

_____

Romans 15:1 also emphasizes our responsibility to help those in need. Read this verse and record your thoughts here.

_____

_____

_____

The third group of people we are to serve are *our enemies*. Now we may be on board with Jesus' commands to serve others, but this part of His directive may be a bit more challenging. I'm supposed to serve my enemies? Yes, that's part of the "upside-down-ness" of God's Kingdom. It is possibly the dirtiest, smelliest, and most uncomfortable part of serving. Jesus explains this concept in Matthew 5:43-47. What is His command in verse 44?

_____

_____

_____

What is His rationale in verses 45-47?

_____

_____

_____

Similarly, what does Jesus say in Luke 6:35?

_____

_____

_____

What does Paul write in Romans 12:20 about serving your enemies?

_____

_____

_____

The coals of fire likely refer to an Egyptian practice the Israelites observed during their captivity (Exodus 1). A person who was repentant for wrong-doing would carry a dish of burning coals on their head to exhibit their remorse. Therefore, serving your enemy may be a tool in God's hand to convict them and bring them into a right relationship with Him and others.

What is the reward for serving other Christians, people in need, and even our enemies? Proverbs 19:17 gives us some insight. What does it say?

_____

_____

_____

True greatness is marked by authentic service. I wonder how many people we will meet in heaven who were unknown on earth but who served God and others so devoutly that they will be celebrities in eternity. They are the real superstars in the Kingdom of God. How do you serve people who are members of each of these groups?

Other Christians: _____

Those in need: _____

Your enemies: _____

Father, I want to have a heart that aches to serve other people. I need help with serving people, especially my enemies, but I know through Christ I can do all things. Show me a person today whom You want me to serve, and may You receive all glory as the Great God Who serves us with unending love. Amen.

——— DAY 4: HOW DO I SERVE?

I come to You now, Lord, full of needs and questions. I know only You have what I need. Help me to listen carefully to all You say to me during this quiet time alone with You.

There are innumerable ways to serve God by serving other people. Walking in the Spirit's steps ensures we are serving Him as He wants. Prayer is a key to this practice, and praying for others is a way to serve them. For example, I have a list of people I pray for every day. This list includes family members, my First Place for Health members, my church staff, friends, co-workers, and ministry leaders. I ask God to be with each of them and pray for any current needs of which I am aware.

Look up Ephesians 6:18; what does this verse say about praying for others?

_____

_____

_____

Prayer is an important part of serving God and others. Read 1 Timothy 2:1-2. What does Paul encourage us to do and why?

_____

_____

_____

Another important way to serve God is through sharing the gospel with others. What does 1 Timothy 2:3-4 say?

_____

_____

_____

What did Jesus tell His disciples in Acts 1:8?

_____

_____

_____

How does Peter instruct us to witness in 1 Peter 3:15?

_____

_____

_____

As First Place for Health members, we have a story to share that others may be open to hear. Everyone is interested in how to lose weight. We can talk about our own struggle with weight loss and healthy eating and how God is a part of that journey. What is one thing you can share with someone that will open a way for you to share God's offer of salvation?

_____

_____

_____

A third way we serve God and others is through practical acts of meeting people's needs. These acts of kindness can be inside or outside the church community. Read Hebrews 10:24-25 and describe how our church gatherings can impact our Christian service.

_____

_____

_____

How are you serving God in practical ways, either in your church or the general community?

_____

_____

_____

Author Rick Warren notes the mark of spiritual maturity occurs when a believer "takes off the bib and puts on an apron."[2] We "put on an apron" and serve God by praying for others and meeting their physical, emotional, mental, and spiritual needs as we are led by the Spirit. None of those things is for our own glory but for His Kingdom's sake. What is one thing you will do this week that will serve God by serving others?

_____

_____

Thank You for serving me, Father, through Your love, sacrifice, and ministry to me through Your Spirit. Give me opportunities to share Your love and serve others, and keep me faithful to serving You as You direct me. Amen.

—— DAY 5: WHY DO I SERVE?

How I long to meet with You today, O Lord. I want to be permeated by Your presence and saturated with Your Spirit. My heart yearns for more of You.

Serving God is not an option if you desire to follow Jesus. But we don't serve out of compulsion. We serve out of love: love for God and love for others. We follow Jesus' model of sacrificial love when serving others is a priority. God's Word encourages us to develop a loving servant's heart. Read the following scriptures and record how each one inspires you to love and serve.

Scripture	Inspiration to Love and Serve
Romans 12:10-11	
1 Corinthians 16:14	
Ephesians 2:10	
1 Peter 2:16	

1 John 4:19 gives us the reason we love God. What is that reason?

_____

_____

_____

What do verses 20-21 tell us about loving others?

_____

_____

_____

It is easy to let love be replaced by pride as our motivation to serve. As we make progress on our fitness goals, we may receive compliments that can go to our heads. We may forget that the only reason we are successful is that God gives us the strength and desire to make healthy choices. As we serve others, we must ensure that He gets all the glory. We can do that by keeping our eyes firmly fixed on Him. We can also remember that service stems from what Jesus does for us, not what we do for Him. We love and serve Him because He loves and serves us.

What is your motivation for serving God and others? How do you know this is true?

_____

_____

_____

Timothy Stackpole faced a crossroads in his life in 1998. He was a firefighter, and he was recovering from severe burns suffered in a fire. His family and friends urged him to retire from firefighting, and he could have taken that route and lived comfortably. But he was passionate about serving others by fighting fires, and when he was able, he returned to the work. He was promoted to captain due to his outstanding leadership. One day his crew received a call to assist a startling disaster. He led his team into the second tower of the World Trade Center in New York after a plane had crashed into the first tower. On September 11, 2001, Captain Timothy Stackpole paid the ultimate price for service when the second tower collapsed. His life exemplifies service motivated by love for others.

What does Jesus say in John 15:12-13?

_____

Father, I want to have a servant's heart, free from pride and selfishness, totally devoted to You. Use Your Word and Your Spirit to inspire me to serve others with the same love You have for me, to see others through Jesus' eyes. Help me lay down my life as Jesus did. Amen.

—— DAY 6: REFLECTION AND APPLICATION

As I meet with You, dear Father, open my heart and mind to receive Your words to me today. I am weary from the work and worry in my world. I need Your peace and comfort.

Jamila Jackson wanted to have a family. For as long as she could remember, being a mother was the vision she had for her life. But after five years of trying and a miscarriage, she and her husband were still not parents. Jamila says that she began a season of praying and fasting, and during those deep times, God revealed a new vision. She began to be an encourager to others, and that encouragement became a ministry. Many years later her enterprise, love+blessed, includes a store providing uplifting gifts in pink boxes, a community, a speaking ministry, and a book. Jamila shares that her misery turned to ministry: "If my husband and I are never blessed with children, I still want to leave a legacy. So I pray that with each box we mail, that my legacy will be one of encouragement and my testimony will remind someone that there is nothing you're going through that God can't see you through."[3]

God provides opportunities for our service every day all around us. They can be small acts or something that grows into a full-blown ministry like Jamila. He may take our deepest hurts and turn them into ways to serve others. We just need to be alert and available, continue to show up, and be open to whatever He has planned for us. And there are times when the service may line up with our talents and gifts. Read 1 Peter 4:10. What are we encouraged to do?

_____

_____

_____

God sometimes calls us to serve in ways that are outside our comfort zones. When I was in elementary school, I had terrible penmanship. (Okay, I still do!) My fine motor skills were subpar, and I wrote too fast. The school counselor encouraged my mom to enroll me in summer art classes to improve my dexterity and slow me down. I was also very shy and didn't like being in front of a group of people. When I went to college, I learned sign language and became an interpreter for the hearing impaired. I would stand up in church or in classrooms and sign for the people who couldn't hear. Once I interpreted a small part of a Billy Graham Crusade meeting at Rice Stadium, which seats over seventy thousand people! I would never have imagined that my hands could perform service in this way when they seemed deficient as a child or that God could conquer my shyness so I could stand in front of a crowd.

What service or ministry has God called you to do that involves your talents or gifts?

_____

_____

_____

What service or ministry has God called you to do that involves getting out of your comfort zone? Or has God used an area of pain to give you a platform for praising Him?

_____

_____

_____

Serving others is part of living a balanced and healthy life as a Christ follower. As we consider progressing toward our fitness goals, we can include service as a way to put Christ first as well as nourishment for our spirits, souls, minds, and bodies. It is satisfying to help others, but we are not doing it for our own gratification. We serve because we love God and all people.

Use me, Lord, in any way You want. Use the talents and gifts You have given me. Use me in ways that stretch my abilities. In all these acts of service, may I depend on You and not myself. Give me wisdom and guide me into the steps You have already established for me to walk in, by Your Spirit's power. Amen.

—— DAY 7: REFLECTION AND APPLICATION

Holy Father, I thank You today for Jesus, for His amazing love, His intercession before Your throne on my behalf, and His eminent return. Help me to listen to You now as You teach me how to be more like Him.

This week we have looked at God's better way to greatness in His Kingdom: serving Him and others. Stooping to serve results in rising to royalty. As you reflect on what God has revealed to you during this week, consider how you currently serve and how He might be calling you to serve in new ways. Here are some prompts for your consideration or to put in your journal.

• Review the groups of people Jesus listed in Matthew 25:35-36. How have you served people in these groups in the past? Research how you can serve people in these circumstances in your community. Ask God to show you where He wants you to serve others who represent the needs Jesus talked about.

• Draw a large outline of a heart. Within the heart write words that denote the attitude of a servant of God. You can use scripture verses along with or instead of the words.

• Make a list of ways you have served God in the past, how you are currently serving Him, and ways you would like to serve Him. Pray over this list and ask God for encouragement and wisdom in serving others out of love for Him.

• Find a song that encourages you in this process. You may document the lyrics and record your own reflections on them, or you could illustrate them with sketches or images you locate. Two examples for this week's study are "I Will Serve the Lord" by Nik Day (2021) and "Make Me a Servant" by Kelly Willard (1982).

Your journal is a very private and personal process; therefore, share it carefully. If social media is a healthy place for you, use these hashtags for posting your words, images, other reflections, or personal stories from this study: #fp4h and #fp4habetterway. You can view my journal and others' entries using these hashtags.

I'm thankful that I serve the one true God Who loves me and calls me into partnership in His Kingdom. Father, make me a servant who lovingly and faithfully represents You to the world. May You be glorified by all I do in Your Name and for Christ's sake. Amen.

1 Noel Atkinson. "The Jesus Freaks Are Here." Sermon Central (2011), https://www.sermoncentral.com/sermon-illustrations/78335/servanthood-by-noel-atkinson.

2 Rick Warren, "The Five Marks of Spiritual Maturity," Pastors.com (2022), https://pastors.com/the-five-marks-of-spiritual-maturity/.

3 Jamila Jackson, "He Turned My Misery into Ministry," love+blessed (2017), https://lovedandblessed.com/blogs/encouragement/he-turned-my-misery-into-my-ministry.

WEEK SIX: WALK BY FAITH INSTEAD OF BY SIGHT

SCRIPTURE MEMORY VERSE
For we live by faith, not by sight. 2 Corinthians 5:7

There were once two nuns who were driving a car to the hospital where they worked. They ran out of gas on the road, and a truck driver stopped to help them. He was willing to siphon gas from his truck for them to put in their car, but he didn't have a gas can or other container to transfer the fuel. The nuns checked their trunk and found a bedpan. The truck driver siphoned gas into the bedpan and went on his way. At that time a police car drove by, and the officers saw the nuns with the bedpan by their gas tank. One officer remarked, "I don't think that will work, but I admire their faith!"[1]

This humorous anecdote makes us chuckle, but it does point to the essence of faith. Hebrews 11:1 says, "Now faith is confidence in what we hope for and assurance about what we do not see." The Passion Translation puts it this way: "Now faith brings our hopes into reality and becomes the foundation needed to acquire the things we long for. It is all the evidence required to prove what is still unseen." In the Kingdom of God, faith is the fuel that drives our daily walk. This is the opposite of the world's viewpoint that we can only believe in what we can see.

Last week in *A Better Way*, we considered serving God and others to be honored.
- Jesus showed us throughout His brief, earthly life how a servant becomes great in the Kingdom of God.
- Some of the characteristics of a servant's heart include sacrifice, devotion, and humility.
- Other Christians, people in need, and even our enemies are some of the people we should serve in Jesus' Name.
- We can serve God and others in many ways, including praying, sharing the gospel and our First Place for Health stories, and helping people in practical ways.
- God's Word encourages us to develop a servant's heart that is motivated purely by love.

During this week's study we will investigate the upside-down Kingdom of God's call to walk by faith rather than by sight. As we dive into the faith-walking practice, let's open our minds and hearts to the Spirit's leading. He is our guide in the better ways of living by godly faith.

—— DAY 1: FAITH THAT SEES

I believe that You are with me now, Lord, as I stop to rest a while with You. I know that I will find everything I need as You speak to me through Your Word and Your Spirit.

Write this week's memory verse here.

_____

_____

_____

This verse is in the center of Paul's teaching about being with Jesus in heaven. He wrote that our earthly bodies will be replaced with heavenly ones (2 Corinthians 5:1). We who are on a wellness journey can rejoice that we will get new bodies! And what an upgrade! No more pain, sickness, or brokenness. How do I know this promise is true? Have I seen a person who died and was transformed into a heavenly body? No, I haven't. But I do have eyes of faith that assure me that what Paul describes is true.

Let's look at some faith-walking people who encountered Jesus. Read Mark 10:46-52 and summarize what happened.

_____

_____

_____

What an amazing story of literal blindness being replaced with sight! Bartimaeus had faith that Jesus would heal him. Why did he believe? He had heard about what Jesus had done for others. It was not blind faith; it was trust based on facts. We could speculate that if Bartimaeus had not called out to Jesus that he wouldn't have been healed. That may be why Jesus said, "…your faith has healed you." The people around him told him to be quiet. The world doesn't believe that calling on Jesus will help. But we know He is always with us and answers our prayers because He has done it before.

Another person who encountered Jesus is a non-example of a faith-walker. Read John 20:24-29 and summarize Thomas' story.

_____

_____

_____

Jesus makes an important point here. Faith involves believing in Him even when your senses tell you differently. Even if you do not see how God is with you, He is. If His voice seems silent, He is still speaking to you. If you cannot feel Him holding your hand, you can still be confident in His care and guidance. The spiritual part of life is not revealed through our five senses. It is revealed to us through the Holy Spirit Who lives in us. That's why we can't depend on our sight to walk in faith. What does Hebrews 11:6 tell us about the importance of faith?

GPS (Global Positioning System) is an amazing technology. I can enter an address or a place's name, and the map app on my smart phone will create a path for me to follow. Even if I have never been to this site before, I am confident that if I follow the steps laid out for me, I will arrive where I want to go. Why am I sure? I've used it before and it was successful. I put my faith in GPS because it is consistently correct. It is impossible for me to find the new location on my own. I need the knowledge that the GPS science provides.

The same is true of God. He has shown Himself faithful over and over again: in the Bible, in my life, and in others' lives. I believe in Him, and that pleases Him. Even my salvation is a gift from Him that I receive through faith (Ephesians 2:8-9). Trusting Him is not blind faith; it is faith based on facts. Read the following piece and write a response to it below.

> Walking by faith means living life in light of eternal consequences. To walk by faith is to fear God more than man; to obey the Bible even when it conflicts with man's commands; to choose righteousness over sin, no matter what the cost; to trust God in every circumstance; and to believe God rewards those who seek Him, regardless of who says otherwise. To walk by faith requires that we tune our hearts to the voice of the Holy Spirit and the truth of His Word (John 10:27; 16:13).[2]

Perhaps something in your circumstances looks hopeless. You have been working on losing weight and becoming fit, and you are discouraged by the slow progress or lack of success. You can trust God even though your situation doesn't seem positive and the outcome looks disappointing. He is faithful and worthy of your faith. What do you need to trust God for today?

_____

_____

Thank You, Father, for Your never-ending faithfulness. I know that I can trust You with every part of my life and being. Help me keep my eyes on You, the author and finisher of my faith. Amen.

—— DAY 2: FAITH AND WISDOM

I love You, Lord, and am thankful for this time I can spend with You. Shut out all distractions and focus my mind on You and Your Word, the source of the answers to all my questions.

The Bible study leader directed us to meet in our small groups. We were in a deep study of scripture and theology that required a fair amount of reading outside the class. As we tackled the discussion questions, one person in the group expressed some frustration with the way the class was being taught. He said, "I wish he'd just do a PowerPoint and tell me what I need to know!" As an educator, I became concerned. Have we become such lazy learners that we only receive instruction by PowerPoint without engaging in thinking for ourselves?

I find faith-walking to be a similar situation. It would be so easy if I could open the Bible and just see a specific list of what to do today to follow Jesus. Go to church, check! Read my Bible, check! Pray, check! Those are important habits, but walking in faith requires more than following a to-do list. Let's look at John the Baptist to help us gain insight into this process. We know from Luke 1 that he was born to older parents, that God had called him to proclaim the coming of the Messiah, and that his mother Elizabeth was related to Mary, the mother of Jesus. What does Matthew 3:1-6 tell us about John and his ministry?

_____

_____

_____

What did John say about the coming Messiah in John 1:26-27?

_____

_____

_____

When Jesus came to John at the Jordan River, what did John say about him (verses 29-30)?

_____

_____

How did John know that Jesus was the Messiah (verses 31-34)?

_____

_____

_____

Put yourself in John's sandals for a moment. His cousin is the Messiah? John is only a few months older than Jesus and has known Him all his life. When they were children, he likely played with Jesus at family gatherings. They may have met when their families went to Jerusalem for annual festivals. It would appear from these verses that he had no idea that his cousin Jesus was the Messiah. God waited until just that moment to reveal it to him. John had faithfully followed God's leadership in his life, and God showed him His Son. There was no Messiah Announcer Manual for John to use. He walked in faith with God daily.

There are some important things we can learn from John the Baptist's faith walk. The first is that our faith is a dependable way to live only because we have faith in a dependable God. Even though we can't physically see Jesus as John did, we can trust Him to guide us into the steps He has prepared for us since the beginning of time. What does 1 Thessalonians 5:24 tell us about God's faithfulness?

_____

_____

_____

Say it out loud: "He will do it!" I can choose to look at my circumstances or I can choose to believe that God will do what He promised to do, no matter how long it takes or how impossible it seems right now. How has God been faithful in your life?

_____

_____

_____

Second, we learn that faith walking requires wisdom. Read Romans 10:17; from where do we get wisdom?

_____

_____

_____

It is clear from the way John spoke that he had studied the Torah and the Prophets. God's Word was an important part of his faith walk. John the Baptist knew God's Word and used it in his ministry. In the Hebrew tradition, the idea of physically hearing God's Word included the idea of obedience. There was no hearing unless you also followed what you heard. As we put faith into practice, we learn wisdom. If we have faith in something that is false or unreliable, the strength of our faith cannot make it right. If we have correct knowledge but never act on it, the knowledge is useless. We must believe in God and put the truth of His Word into practice in order to walk in faith with wisdom. How do we know the direction we sense is from God? We must walk daily in conversation with Him through prayer and His Word to know His will and be able to do it.

Third, faith walking is opposed to the world's system. John's lifestyle certainly went against conventional wisdom. His extreme practice as an ascetic was shocking to many people. Religious leaders criticized him. But he trusted God in spite of these obstacles. What does Romans 12:2 tell us about living in faith in contrast to the world's ways?

_____

_____

_____

What does Paul say about the world's standards and God's wisdom in 1 Corinthians 3:18-20?

_____

_____

_____

Faith is an essential ingredient in our wellness journey in First Place for Health. We believe God gives us the strength and power to make healthy choices. We develop wisdom as we listen to His Word through Bible study, daily scripture reading, and prayer, then put it into practice. We reject the world's view of extreme diets and body shaming and instead embrace God's better way of balanced living and worth.

We gather information from the world around us by using our five senses. They are vital to our growth and safety. We can also develop a faith sense, a way to interact with God through the Holy Spirit that guides us into healthy and holy living. Faith requires a process of continually and intentionally communicating with God. It is not a checklist we do on our own but moment-by-moment intimacy with our Creator.

What is one thing you will do this week to further develop your "faith sense?"

_____

_____

_____

Thank You, Father, for being so faithful to me. I want to develop my faith sense so that everything I do is directed by Your Holy Spirit Who lives in me. I reject the world's view of excess and criticism and rejoice in Your discipline and devotion that guide my life. Amen.

—— DAY 3: FAITH AND ACTION

My sweet Lord, I am resting in Your presence. I am hungry for Your Word and Your teachings. I am here to be with You alone and be immersed in Your love.

Yesterday we looked at faith and wisdom and how they work together. Let's explore some practical applications of walking in faith with wisdom as we seek to develop and maintain healthy habits. First, faith does not ignore facts and is not based on feelings. We may imagine that faith is just going with what feels right and thinking that it is the Spirit moving us. It is not an excuse for poor planning. The Spirit can lead us in planning as well as carrying out plans. But it does include flexibility to change plans when we sense God is guiding us in a different direction. We must ask God for discernment and listen to His leading. It doesn't mean we have *no sight*. On the contrary, it means we have *enhanced sight* because we see reality as it is but with a heavenly perspective. Paul and Silas saw their reality in this way. They had been put in prison after healing a woman in Philippi. Read Acts 16:25-28 and describe their experience in the jail cell.

_____

_____

_____

When Paul woke up that morning, going to jail was not on his agenda. He and Silas were aware that they were in a dangerous position and may have faced fears about their circumstances. But they walked in faith by consistently communicating with God, even in the jail, singing and worshipping Him. What was the result of their situation (verses 29-34)?

_____

_____

_____

We may never know the impact of our choices to believe God instead of going our own way. In this case, Paul's and Silas' faith had an eternal Kingdom impact.

A second practical application of walking in faith is our involvement with God's work. Tony Evans has said, "God will always do His part. But He won't do your part. Walking by faith involves action."[3] Although prayer and God's Word are important parts of faith-walking, it doesn't end there. We must put feet to our faith. Last week we studied serving God and others, and faith is a main ingredient of that mindset. Read James 2:14-18. What is the relationship between serving and faith?

_____

_____

_____

Another practical application of following God in faith is the size of our faith. We can have a small amount of faith in a big God and accomplish great things in His Kingdom. It's not the size of our faith that is important; it's the size of our God. Our faith gets stronger the more we use it, just as a muscle does. Once Jesus' disciples tried unsuccessfully to heal a demon-possessed boy. They asked Jesus why they couldn't do it. Look up Matthew 17:20-21 and record Jesus' reply.

_____

_____

_____

Next, the conduit for walking in faith is prayer. Faith doesn't involve saying specific words in a specific order to get God to answer your prayer. It's not some voodoo incantation or magic wand we wield, demanding God perform miracles at our discretion. It is a daily interaction with God to gain power and knowledge to follow Him completely. How did Jesus describe this kind of faith in Matthew 21:21-22?

_____

_____

_____

Finally, faith-walking is an essential part of battling the enemy. As we practice making healthy choices, faith helps us combat temptation and protects us from attack. What does Ephesians 6:16 tell us about the role of faith in spiritual warfare?

_____

_____

_____

We have looked at these practical aspects of walking in faith rather than by sight.
- Faith does not ignore facts and is not based on feelings.
- Faith means being personally involved with God's work.
- The size of our God is more important than the size of our faith.
- The conduit for walking in faith is prayer.
- Faith-walking is an essential part of battling the enemy.

Which of these practical applications of faith is most meaningful to you at this point in your life? Why?

_____

_____

_____

Let's end today's time in God's Word with part of a prayer that Jesus prayed for us only hours before the arrest that led to His crucifixion. He was thinking of you as He faced torture and a painful death. What great love He has for us!

"My prayer is not for [my disciples] alone. I pray also for those who will believe in me through their message [that's you!], that all of them may be one, Father, just as you are in me and I am in you. May they also be in us *so that the world may believe* that You have sent me. I have given them the glory that you gave me, that they may be one as we are one— I in them and you in me—so that they may be brought to complete unity. Then *the world will know that you sent me* and have loved them even as you have loved me." John 17:20-23 (Emphasis and note added.)

My loving Father, thank You for loving me and giving me faith to believe in You and to walk with Jesus. Help me to understand the importance of faith in every moment of my life. May I follow You completely, for I want to walk only in the steps You have prepared for me. Amen.

—— DAY 4: FAITH AND OBEDIENCE

Today is a great day to be Your child, Father. I want to get closer to You and know You more. Speak to me during this quiet time with You.

The flood waters were raging around Farmer Jones' home. He stood on his porch and saw a boat on its way to rescue him. As the man in the boat pulled up and called out, "Let me take you to safety," Farmer Jones said, "I'm trusting God to save me." The man in the boat left. The waters continued to rise until Farmer Jones had to move to the second story of his house. Another boat neared him and a man shouted, "I can take you to a Red Cross shelter." Farmer Jones refused, saying, "I'm trusting God to save me," so the boat went away. As the water rose even more, the safe place was the roof. A helicopter flew overhead and dropped a ladder to him, and the pilot screamed at Farmer Jones, "Quick! Grab the ladder so I can get you safely out of this flood!" But Farmer Jones yelled back, "I'm trusting God to save me." The pilot flew away to help other people in peril. Eventually, the wind and water overcame Farmer Jones and sadly, he drowned. When he arrived in heaven, he entered God's presence. God seemed surprised to see him. "What are you doing here, Farmer Jones?" "I put my trust in you," he replied, "but you let me down." God stated, "What are you talking about? I sent you two boats and a helicopter!"[3]

When God gives us answers to our prayers for direction and help, we have to listen and obey. Obedience is not a popular practice. We are more likely to do things our own way then ask God's blessings on our independent choices. "Please, God, don't let the scale show the unhealthy choices I made this week." It is hard to put feet to our faith if we are not willing to obey the God in Whom we trust. Look up Proverbs 3:5-6 and write it here.

_____

_____

_____

The Message puts it this way: "Trust God from the bottom of your heart; don't try to figure out everything on your own. Listen for GOD's voice in everything you do, everywhere you go; he's the one who will keep you on track." My First Place for Health class members often ask for prayer to "get back on track," meaning to make healthy choices with their food and exercise. To be "on track," we must trust and obey.

What would it look like if we prayed for God to make us obedient in our faith walk? When we pray, do we want God to fix our circumstances or fix us? I heard this idea recently, and it really has me thinking. God is not interested in making my life easy; He is interested in making me like Jesus. He wisely knows that my spiritual growth is more likely to thrive when I'm trusting in Him for everything. Sometimes I need to see how life looks when He is the only option I have.

Notice that Proverbs 3:5-6 does not say, "Trust in the Lord with all your heart, and everything will turn out well." Faith walking doesn't ensure positive outcomes every day. We know we will have struggles as we live in a broken world and as we make mistakes. Faithful allegiance to Jesus means I follow Him anyway, anywhere, no matter what the cost. He promises to be with me despite the circumstances.

In this Old Testament context *heart* includes the idea of your entire inner being, even your appetites. "Trust in the Lord with all your appetites" is a relevant concept in First Place for Health. I can choose to channel my appetite for food into cravings for God and His goodness. I can't trust God with my whole heart and lean on my own understanding at the same time. And *all* means "all." Nothing held back. All my heart, all my ways, submitted 100 percent to Him, practicing obedience daily.

When it comes to God's better way of walking in faith instead of by sight, I must learn to move forward. If I take one step of faith and obey, then God will show me the next step.

Look up Psalm 119:105, and record it here.

_____

_____

Think about the lamps the Israelite people used during this ancient time without electrical sources of light. They were small containers of oil with a wick; when they were lit, they gave off some light, but at night it would be only enough light to see one step in front of you. God asks you to trust Him with the next step, to take the step He is showing you even though you don't know what comes after that. One step at a time obedience is what walking by faith really means. And God can more easily guide a person who is already in motion. As we obediently take each step, He will guide us as we trust in Him.

What does faith walking look like in your life? How are you walking steps of faith and how does that impact your efforts to make healthy choices?

_____

_____

_____

How do you find faith in God impacts your struggles to obey Him in all things?

_____

_____

_____

Dear friend, remember that God adores you and wants only the best for you. You can obediently follow Him in faith, knowing He is on a mission to deliver you and bless you, one step at a time.

Thank You, my Father, for Your faithful guidance in my life. I want to focus my appetites on You and not my own fleshly desires. Give me wisdom to obey You each step of my journey, knowing You always choose what is best for me. Amen.

—— DAY 5: FAITH LEAPING

Hello, dear Lord. I'm grateful for this time to pull away from crowded thoughts and frantic activities so I can sit in Your presence. Open my eyes and heart to Your teachings for me.

I confess that I suffer from basophobia, which is a fancy way to say I have a fear of falling. I'm not so bothered by heights; if I'm up high but within a secure place, I'm not concerned. But if I'm standing on a stool, I can panic at the feeling that I may fall. It is possible to have spiritual basophobia, a fear of falling as I choose to walk by faith rather than sight. Today we will explore how we can be bold in our faith walk, ready to take a leap of faith when God calls us.

Jesus often asked His disciples to take leaps of faith as He proclaimed the Kingdom of God. One example is recorded in Matthew 14. Let's set the scene: Jesus learned about John the Baptist's execution and drew away from the crowds to be alone and grieve. Read Matthew 14:13-17 and describe the situation that followed.

_____

_____

_____

The disciples saw the realistic limitations they faced. There were over five thousand people to feed, there were no markets from which to buy food, they had no funds to feed that many people, and the only food at their disposal was five loaves of bread and two fish. They only saw the scarcity of their situation. Yet Jesus told them to take a leap of faith, to trust Him, to feed the people. Read verses 18-21 and summarize the outcome.

_____

_____

_____

The disciples did follow Jesus' directions, even though they were likely confused about how the loaves and fishes would meet the people's needs. If they had put their faith in the food, they would have failed. They did put their faith in Jesus, Who filled the people's stomachs and twelve baskets. Their leap of faith resulted in miraculous provision.

Jesus challenged another person to take a leap of faith. Read Mark 9:14-18. What did the father want the disciples to do?

_____

_____

_____

Read verses 19-23. What did Jesus tell the man in verse 23?

_____

_____

_____

How did the man reply (verse 24)?

_____

_____

_____

The man was honest about his reluctance to take the leap of faith Jesus asked him to make: "Help my unbelief!" How often we too need to recognize our reluctance to believe, when we cling to the familiar rather than step out into what may seem like thin air. What happened in verses 25-27?

_____

_____

_____

Jesus showed the man that taking the leap of faith He had guided him to take was worth the risk. Although His disciples and the religious leaders had been unable to help him, Jesus gave the father his request. Focusing on Jesus always results in victory, whether it's miraculous revelation or peace in the storm.

Read 1 John 5:4-5 to learn what results from our faith in Christ.

_____

_____

_____

You have already overcome the world, so you can feel confident in faith leaping. God may ask you to do something that you can do through faith in Him alone. And when He does, He's there with you. We can let go of everything that keeps us from trusting Him and be free to live by faith and not by sight. We can choose faith over fear and still feel afraid while acting in faith. God will give us peace as we choose to walk in His steps.

In her book *Surrendered*, Barb Roose states an important principle: "I choose to live by faith, not to rush to follow my feelings."[4] Our feelings can mislead us as we walk by faith and not by sight. We need to recognize our feelings and process them in healthy ways. But we have to be careful not to take a leap of feelings rather than a leap of faith. Daily prayer and Bible study can also help us develop our spiritual senses to follow God's leadership rather than our emotions.

Is God asking you to take a leap of faith? If so, what is it? What do you need to help you step out in faith?

_____

_____

_____

God, I know part of my walk with You is to take a leap of faith now and then. I confess I like to stay in my comfort zone and resist stepping out into uncertain situations. Help me to trust You and follow where You lead me, knowing You are the God Who loves me. Amen.

—— DAY 6: REFLECTION AND APPLICATION

How I love You, Lord, my Father God, my all in all. You are the light in my heart and the joy in my soul. Speak to my inmost being, sweet Lord.

In 1981 I met a group of faith-walkers at Houston's First Baptist Church. They had just begun a new ministry called First Place. The purpose of this enterprise was to empower God's people to put Him first in all areas of their lives, especially in the area of eating and fitness. I joined my first group in September, and God has used this amazing ministry in my life ever since. I will always be grateful for His calling and for the people who started First Place, for the leap of faith they took in answering God's direction. After over 40 years, the ministry has grown far beyond those first few groups of people, and thousands of lives have been changed from the inside out.

There are several things I've learned about walking in faith through God's leadership in First Place for Health. One is illustrated by a story in 2 Kings 6:8-23. Here's the background: the king of Aram was coming to capture the prophet Elisha at Dothan because he had been responsible for keeping the Arameans from defeating the Israelites.

Read 2 Kings 6:15. What did Elisha's servant observe and say about the enemy?

_____

_____

_____

What was Elisha's reply to his servant in verse 16?

_____

_____

Walking by faith is harder to do when you go it alone. God provides people to walk alongside us in our wellness journeys, and we are blessed to have First Place for Health members who cheer us on and whom we also support. The fellowship I have with the people in my classes and within the larger First Place for Health community is amazing and has contributed immensely to my faith walk. How does your First Place for Health community help you walk by faith?

_____

_____

_____

Another aspect of walking by faith involves a principle found in 1 Corinthians 2:4-5. Read these verses and identify the foundation of our faith.

_____

_____

_____

A lifestyle of making consistent, healthy choices cannot be sustained by our own strength. We cannot succeed using our white-knuckled willpower to resist tempting, unhealthy food and practices. It only happens through God's power, and we access it through faith in Him, believing that He can and will do it through His Spirit working in us.

A third principle I've learned is expressed in Jude 1:3. Look up this verse and identify what Jude says about our faith.

_____

_____

_____

Walking by faith requires intentional, consistent work. It is not a feeling that comes over us like magic and results in healthy living. It is daily work, practicing the habits we develop in First Place for Health: reading and studying the Bible, memorizing scripture, following the food plan, recording what you eat in the food diary, praying, contacting prayer partners, exercising, and attending weekly meetings. How do developing these habits help you contend for your faith in God?

_____

_____

_____

One of Jesus' repeated questions in His teachings was, "Do you have eyes to see and ears to hear?" We understand His Word and His Spirit's work in us through faith. Faith gives us the eyes to see and ears to hear, and through faith we put His Word into practice in our lives. How will you practice faith this week to develop your spiritual senses?

_____

_____

_____

Thank You, Father, for the faith You give us to trust You more each day. Help me to learn how to contend for my faith, walking with others and accessing Your power to make healthy choices and to be a good steward of all the parts of my being. I love You and want to follow You alone. Amen.

—— DAY 7: REFLECTION AND APPLICATION

Father, I bow in Your presence now, anticipating Your prompting in my heart to yield to You, allowing You to do whatever it is You desire in my life right now.

We've studied God's better way of walking by faith and not by sight this week. What thoughts and questions are you contemplating about this part of living in God's upside-down Kingdom? Use today's time and the prompts below to go deeper in this study about faith walking.

• Make a two-column chart. Title one side "Sight" and the other side "Faith." Under each heading, list things in your life that represent walking by sight and walking by faith. End with a prayer asking God for help to deepen your faith walk and to leave behind walking by sight alone.

• Review these questions from Day 4: What would it look like if we prayed for God to make us obedient in our faith walk? When we pray, do we want God to fix our circumstances or fix us? Write responses to these questions and make personal connections to your current circumstances and ways you can pray in faith.

• Keep a daily faith journal. Record the ways God calls you to trust Him and how respond to His calls.

• Find a song that encourages you in this process. You may document the lyrics and record your own reflections on them, or you could illustrate them with sketches or images you locate. Two examples for this week's study are "Walk by Faith" by Jeremy Camp (2002) and "By Faith" by Keith and Kristyn Getty (2009).

Your journal is a very private and personal process; therefore, share it carefully. If social media is a healthy place for you, use these hashtags for posting your words, images, other reflections, or personal stories from this study: #fp4h and #fp4habetterway. You can view my journal and others' entries using these hashtags.

Father, my faith in You is vital to my life and who I am. I want to walk by faith and not by sight by trusting and obeying You. Give me wisdom and insight into how I should pray and how I should live to honor and glorify You, the Author and Finisher of my faith. Amen.

1 Daniel McCoy, "Walk by Faith, Not Sight: What It Means, What It Doesn't," Renew.org (2023), https://renew.org/walk-by-faith-not-sight/.
2 "What Does It Mean to Walk by Faith Not by Sight?" Got Questions (2023), https://www.gotquestions.org/walk-by-faith-not-by-sight.html.
3 Tony Evans, (2022),: https://twitter.com/drtonyevans/status/1596864646291472384.
4 "God Sent the Boats and the Helicopter," Emotional Freedom Techniques (2023), https://www.eftzone.com/2005/02/20/god-sent-the-boats-and-helicopter/.
5 Roose, B. (2020). Surrendered. Nashville: Abingdon Press, p. 3..

WEEK SEVEN: EMBRACE TRIALS TO BECOME JOYFUL

SCRIPTURE MEMORY VERSE

Consider it all joy, my brothers and sisters, when you encounter various trials, knowing that the testing of your faith produces endurance. And let endurance have its perfect result, so that you may be perfect and complete, lacking in nothing. James 1:2-4 NASB

She looked around her, and everyone else was kneeling. In the crowd, she alone was standing. The Japanese government had occupied Korea and demanded that all people bow down and worship their idols. But Ahn Ei Sook refused. She was a Christian and was dedicated to serve God alone. Even after her arrest and six years of torture in a prison camp, even with the threat of execution, Ahn Ei Sook stayed faithful to God, finding peace and joy in her commitment to Him. God was with her and provided for her throughout her imprisonment. When the Japanese lost control of Korea in 1945, the prison camp was emptied and Ahn Ei Sook, along with others who had been incarcerated for their faith in Christ, was released. According to one source, a prison guard said these words about Ahn Ei Sook and her fellow persecuted Christians: "Ladies and gentlemen! These are the ones who for six long years refused to worship Japanese gods. They fought against severe torture, hunger and cold, and have won without bowing their heads to the idol worship of Japan. Today they are champions of the faith!"[1]

Ahn Ei Sook learned and lived an important principle about God's Kingdom life in a sinful world: joy is found in God alone. Even in the most horrific circumstances, she chose joy in Jesus rather than despair or hatred during her imprisonment.

Last week in *A Better Way*, we studied living by faith and not by sight.
* God is faithful and worthy of our faith.
* Faith-walking with a dependable God requires wisdom that is opposed to the world's way of living.
* Faith does not ignore facts and is not based on feelings; we must put feet to our faith; a small amount of faith in a big God can accomplish great things; and prayer is the conduit for walking in faith which is an essential part of battling the enemy.

- When God gives us answers to our prayers for direction and help, we must listen and obey.
- When God asks us to take a leap of faith, He will be with us and it will be worth the risks.

This week we will examine God's better way of thriving during seasons of trials by embracing joy. In Jesus' upside-down Kingdom, our joy is not found in our circumstances but in the presence of God, our true source of joy.

—— DAY 1: TRANSFORMATIVE TRIALS

Here I am, Lord, ready to hear Your words of love and wisdom. I need to feed on Your Word and find my strength in You.

The book of James starts out a bit abruptly. James was writing to Jewish Christians during the early years of the church, and they were going through very difficult times. They were being persecuted because of their faith in Jesus, mainly by non-Christian Jews. After one verse of introducing himself as "a bondservant of God and the Lord Jesus Christ" and addressing his audience, he got right to the point. Practice learning our memory verses for this week, James 1:2-4.

_____

_____

_____

What a radical directive! Imagine you are one of these Jewish Christians. You have chosen to follow Jesus although it means you will face severe persecution. Your family may have disowned you and consider you dead. You are estranged from Jewish friends who are not Jesus followers. You may suffer economic, social, or political losses. And James is telling you to "count it all joy"? Today we will learn how this is possible.

Circle the phrase "the testing of your faith produces endurance." If we understand that trials transform us, it can help us to embrace them. Let's look at a few of the words in this verse and examine their Greek origins.

- *Count* in Greek includes the idea of governing. It's as if we are ruling over our thoughts and emotions, changing our perspective of our trials.
- *Encounter* in Greek includes the idea of falling into the hands of or to strike. It may seem we are walking along and suddenly fall into a pit, or that the trials unexpectedly slap us in the face.

- *Trials* in Greek includes the idea of putting to the proof or proving that something is true. Our reactions to the trials that inevitably befall us reveal the depth of our faith in Jesus.[2]

We all have trials. It is part of life for everyone, Christians and non-Christians alike. We can't avoid them but with the Holy Spirit's help, we can govern our thoughts about our trials. In the upside-down Kingdom of God, we choose to embrace trials and experience joy rather than fight against them and despair. This mindset doesn't ignore the feelings that pain and suffering cause. But through healthy processes, we can give those feelings to God and continue to experience joy. Joy is different from happiness. Happiness is dependent on circumstances. Joy is found in God alone because we have hope and peace in Him, regardless of our situations.

How do you respond to trials? Think of a time you were faced with a trial. How did you handle it?

_____

_____

_____

Read 1 Peter 1:6-7. How does Peter encourage us to rejoice in our trials?

_____

_____

_____

Both Peter and James ask us to focus on the results of our trials. They transform us so that we are "mature, lacking in nothing" and prove "the genuineness of our faith." Chuck Swindoll puts it this way: "Christians evidence their faith by walking in certain ways and not others. For James, a faith that does not produce real life change is a faith that is worthless."[3] James adds another benefit of embracing trials in James 1:12. What does he say?

_____

_____

_____

Hebrews 12:11 gives us additional insight into embracing trials. How does it describe trials and what are the results?

_____

_____

_____

You may have just exited a season of trials or are currently in the midst of a trial. The stress we experience in difficult times can be a trigger that leads to unhealthy behaviors, including binge eating and lack of exercise. Although the trials may seem deep and dark, Jesus is there with us and gives us the opportunity to embrace our trials, knowing that He can use them to transform us. This is not an easy task. When I am hurting, all I want is for the pain to go away. But I have found that Jesus is enough. He soothes my hurt, calms my fears, and helps me endure the trials. I may be battle-scarred and exhausted, but I persevere with His help.

What difficulties are you currently facing? How can you choose to "consider it all joy," with God's help?

_____

_____

_____

Father, I face enormous challenges every day and they threaten to overwhelm me. I understand that You can use these trials to transform me. Help me to process my hurt feelings in healthy ways, not by turning to food or other means of escape. I can trust You with my life, and You will change me if I yield to You. Amen.

—— DAY 2: DEPENDENCE VERSUS INDEPENDENCE

I come to You now, Father, with an open heart that needs Your touch and an open mind ready to receive Your wisdom. Speak Your words of power and strength to me now.

From the moment a baby is born, her parents' job is to help her become independent of them. She is taught to eat, walk, talk, interact socially, and accomplish various tasks so that she will one day be able to live on her own without her parents' supervision. Growing as a Christian is the opposite of this process. As we learn more about God and grow closer to Him, we learn to be more dependent on Him, not less. This concept contradicts the world system, which celebrates those who have succeeded and stand tall on their own.

Through trials, we can develop a deeper dependence on God. During difficulties we can find a closer connection to God, because we are searching for answers to our problems. We learn that only He can truly empathize and offer help when we are at our lowest. Job certainly knew this truth. He is the first person who comes to mind when we think of suffering. Even in the midst of his pain and confusion, he continued talking to God and looking to Him for answers and comfort.

Read Job 35:10. What did God give Job in the midst of his trials ("night")?

_____

_____

_____

A few months after the birth of our second child, my husband, our two young children, and I moved away from our friends and family. I stayed home with my children and had little support or socialization with others. After four months, my husband said he didn't want to be married anymore, and we separated. During those difficult times of loneliness and despair, I grew very dependent on God. He truly was all I had to keep me going. His comfort was always with me. I was never alone. Read the following verses and record what you read about God's constant presence in your life.

Psalm 73:26

_____

_____

_____

Matthew 28:20

_____

_____

_____

Revelation 3:20

_____

_____

_____

Unlike our earthly parents, God our Father wants us to grow more dependent on Him rather than become independent of Him. Jesus modeled this lifestyle for us. Look up John 5:19 and describe Jesus' dependence on God.

_____

_____

_____

We can embrace our trials because we know they bring us closer to God and help us depend on Him more. True joy is found here, because as we climb up into our Father's lap and ask Him to heal our hurts, He embraces us with arms of love and comfort. His presence is where true joy abides. What pain or hurt do you need to bring to God, depending on Him for all you need?

_____

_____

_____

My precious Father, thank You for teaching me how to depend on You and not myself. It is so easy for me to go my own way in my own strength. Help me see that through my trials You are making me more dependent on You and yield myself joyfully to You. Amen.

—— DAY 3: PURPOSE IN TRIALS

The challenges in my life are great, Lord. At times I feel overwhelmed and out of control. My time with You every day is vital as You prepare me for the tasks ahead. Strengthen me now, O Lord.

Sometimes the unbelievable happens and a good person suffers great loss. A former student who had helped start "See You at the Pole" at our middle school was killed in a freak car accident when she was in high school. Our community was shocked and heart-broken. She was a strong Christian and a brilliant student--well-liked by everyone. Why would God allow her to die with such a bright future ahead of her? One of the great questions people have when it comes to God is, "Why do bad things happen to good people?" The world's system believes that good people should only experience rewards for their goodness and bad people should only have hurt and pain. In fact, during biblical times, if you had a disease or if a calamity befell you, others thought you had done something wrong to deserve it (John 9:2).

However, following God does not protect us from suffering. In fact, Jesus promised it. "In this world you will have trouble. But take heart! I have overcome the world" (John 16:33). Yet we can find joy during our trials because we know God can use them for His purposes, both in our lives and in His Kingdom's work, bringing others to Him. Read the following verses to find purposes in our sufferings.

Scripture	Purpose in Sufferings
Job 23:10	
Psalm 119:67	
2 Corinthians 12:7	
Ephesians 1:11	
Hebrews 12:7	
1 Peter 1:6-7	

Knowing that our trials have a purpose in God's hands can make the suffering more bearable. In fact, it can help us thrive during trials, not just survive. We will still have pain, and we can process that pain in healthy ways. It is not done with a flippant attitude that embraces trials, ignoring pain and reality. But in spite of the pain, we put our hope and faith in God that no matter what happens, He is with us and will bring us through to the other side of the trial.

A verse that is often quoted when trials arise is Romans 8:28. Write it here:

_____

_____

_____

Notice that this verse does not say that God thinks suffering is good. It does not say that God causes suffering. It does not explain to us why a good God allows good people to suffer. But reading the entire book of Romans, especially chapter 8, gives us better context for this verse and God's whole mission in the world. He wants to save every person and give them life through His Spirit living in them. He is at work in a world that suffers because all of us sin (Romans 3:23). God uses the suffering we create in this world to accomplish His purpose: salvation for everyone.

When the Christian student from my school died, an assembly was held at the high school to remember and honor her. During that assembly, the gospel was shared because it was so much a part of who she was. We cannot know the full impact that message had on the entire high school community, but we can see at least one purpose her life served in God's Kingdom. This understanding can help us find joy in suffering, knowing that God's ultimate mission can be served. Your suffering may be the one thing that God can use to reach someone for Christ.

Perhaps you have experienced a trial that God used in some way in your life or someone else's life to reveal Himself or bring someone to salvation. Or maybe you know about a situation in someone else's life that God used for His purposes. If so, describe that situation.

_____

_____

_____

How does knowing God uses suffering for His purposes provide perspective as you face trials?

_____

_____

_____

Jesus gives us encouragement in John 14:27: "Peace I leave with you; my peace I give you. I do not give to you as the world gives. Do not let your hearts be troubled and do not be afraid." May His peace empower you to embrace your trials and find joy in Him.

Dear Father, I am amazed at how You can use something bad for a good purpose. I understand that suffering is inevitable, and I can choose to embrace it or resist it. Only You can give me faith during the dark times as I seek You first, even in suffering. Thank You for Your faithful love. Amen.

—— DAY 4: PERMANENT JOY
Dear Lord, my heart is restless because of all the challenges I'm facing. Still my inner being as I approach Your throne of grace to receive Your touch and Your words.

Annie Johnson Flint experienced enormous challenges in her life. She was orphaned as a child, and her adoptive parents died when she was in her twenties. She was diagnosed with debilitating arthritis as a young adult and spent her life in a wheelchair in a care facility. Even though painful joints were a daily reality, she began writing poems and making hand-made cards, many of them in gratitude for those who cared for her.

Every stroke of her pen cost her dearly as she suffered unending pain. As her poems became public, publishers distributed her writings through booklets and magazines. Throughout her lifetime, she wrote thousands of works. Her poems were focused on God's goodness, not her own suffering. She is credited with writing the lyrics for over six thousand hymns, including "He Giveth More Grace." Here are some of the words.

> He giveth more grace as the burdens grow greater.
> He sendeth more strength when the labors increase;
> To added afflictions He addeth His mercy,
> To multiplied trials His multiplied peace.[4]

Annie's pain and suffering was permanent. There was no relief from her physical pain for over 40 years. She had no family to care for her, and she often had financial concerns. Yet her poems and her life reveal that she found joy in God. She believed God had set her aside for a purpose, and she served Him faithfully. She showed us that joy is permanent even in the midst of extreme trials. Our joy is permanent because our God is everlasting and faithful.

How do we access this permanent joy? One answer to this question is found in John 15, part of Jesus' final words to His disciples before His death and resurrection. Look up John 15:1-5 and summarize Jesus' teaching about Himself and His followers.

_____

_____

_____

What is the purpose of pruning (verse 2)?

_____

_____

Why did He tell His disciples these things (verse 11)?

_____

_____

Our constant connection to Jesus is the key to finding permanent joy. He promised His disciples that they would suffer persecution because they chose to follow Him. Paul and Barnabas constantly experienced these trials in their missionary work. Read Acts 13:50-52. What was their reaction to the persecution they suffered?

_____

_____

_____

Turn to 2 Corinthians 8:1-4. How did the Macedonian Christians exhibit joy in their suffering?

_____

_____

_____

Jesus modeled this principle for us in His own life. Imagine the suffering He constantly faced. He was God but chose to experience our humanity, was tempted to sin but never sinned, was abandoned by everyone at His arrest, and died a painful, shameful death on a cross. Read Hebrews 12:1-3. Who is cheering us on?

_____

_____

_____

Why did Jesus endure the cross?

_____

_____

_____

What do you think "the joy set before Him" means (verse 2)?

_____

_____

_____

How do His life and death encourage you to embrace your trials and choose joy?

_____

_____

_____

Psalm 30:5 says, "For his anger lasts only a moment, but his favor lasts a lifetime; weeping may stay for the night, but rejoicing comes in the morning." David wrote these lines in honor of the Temple that would be built and dedicated after his death. He was looking forward to the joy set before him. God had promised him that his son would build the temple he longed to build himself. He had experienced God's deliverance over and over and had learned to trust Him for joy in the midst of his trials. The man after God's own heart had found permanent joy in the constant presence of God. May we be inspired by Annie Johnson Flint, Paul and Barnabas, the Macedonian Christians, David, and most of all, by Jesus as we embrace our trials and find permanent joy in our God.

I am encouraged by Your Word and the lives of people who have followed You in spite of severe suffering. Jesus has given all for me; help me give my all to Him as I embrace my trials and experience everlasting joy. Amen.

——— DAY 5: ETERNAL JOY
Please meet with me now, Holy Lord, as I seek Your face and Your filling. Take this time we have together and change me. Give me the desires of my heart as I commit my ways to You.

There once was a rich man who was dying. He had accumulated great wealth during his life and was sad that he couldn't bring it with him to heaven. He begged God to allow him to bring his fortune, so God permitted him to bring a suitcase full of gold. When the man died and arrived at heaven's door, carrying his suitcase, an angel asked him what he had brought. The man said, "God said I could bring a suitcase full of gold." The angel looked puzzled and asked, "Why did you bring street pavement with you?"

This story references the idea that heaven's streets are paved with gold and that our riches on earth are worthless when compared to the treasures of heaven. There is nothing here on earth that can match the joy and fulfillment that awaits us in God's eternal presence. We will be given new bodies and a special name. We will live with Him forever with no sin or pain. This reality can give us much hope as we face trials and suffering in this life, because we know we will soon walk on streets of gold in God's forever Kingdom of love and light.

Although there are few details in the Bible about what heaven will look like, there are many passages that give us encouragement to focus on our heavenly destination in the midst of trouble. Read 1 Peter 1:3-5 and fill in the blanks. (The verses below come from the NIV translation; you can reword it to match your responses if you use a different version.)

Praise be to the God and Father of our _____ _____ _____! In his great _____ he has given us _____ _____ into a living _____ through the _____ of Jesus Christ from the dead, and into an _____ that can never perish, spoil or fade. This _____ is kept in heaven for _____, who through faith are _____ by God's power until the coming of the _____ that is ready to be revealed in the _____ _____ .

Turn to Matthew 5:11-12, the two verses that end the Beatitudes. In verse 11, Jesus tells us we are blessed when what happens?

_____

_____

_____

In verse 12 what reason does He give us to rejoice?

_____

_____

Notice that in verses 1-10, Jesus said "blessed are those." But in these two verses He says "blessed are *you*." Persecution is personal and painful, and this address to us directly comforts us. If we live as a citizen of God's upside-down Kingdom, exemplifying the beatitudes He teaches in verses 1-10, we will be persecuted. But Jesus said there is blessing even in the trials and our reward in heaven will be great.

How does 2 Corinthians 4:17 describe our troubles?

_____

What are our troubles achieving?

_____

In verse 18 what does Paul encourage us to do?

_____

Read James 1:12 and Revelation 2:10. What are we promised as a result of the suffering we experience on earth?

_____

In Hebrews 10:33-35 we are given encouragement in our trials. What do these verses say about suffering and rewards?

_____

_____

_____

We can embrace our trials because we have been promised an eternity of joy. How does a heavenly perspective help you endure the trials you face today?

_____

_____

_____

Write a prayer thanking God for His blessings, now and in heaven, even the trials that you face.

_____

_____

_____

God, although it is painful to suffer through trials, I have hope because You have promised me a victor's crown of life and a heavenly home. Give me courage and hope as I live each day, knowing my true home is with You. Amen.

—— DAY 6: REFLECTION AND APPLICATION

I find my strength and purpose in You, my Lord. This time each day is precious as I draw strength from You for the day's assignments. I'm listening now for Your voice.

Practice this week's memory verses here.

_____

_____

_____

We've examined two verses this week that use a metaphor of refining gold. Take a moment to review those verses: 1 Peter 1:7 and Job 23:10. Today we will examine why this image of refining gold important for us to understand as we reflect on embracing our trials to experience joy.

In its raw state gold ore is mixed with many other substances. In order to get it to a pure state, it must be refined. It is heated to an extreme temperature, over two thousand degrees Fahrenheit in order to melt. Similarly, God can use our trials as the extreme heat that removes impurities from our lives, including past pains and sins.

Once it is refined, gold is valuable for use in industry because of its properties. It is easy to change its shape. Smoothing out only one ounce of gold can cover up to three hundred square feet. It can be molded into detailed shapes. It conducts electricity, and it doesn't tarnish. As God uses our trials to refine us, He makes us more useful for the purposes of growing His Kingdom.

One way gold is used is to make fine jewelry, but in its pure form it is too soft. In order to create valuable treasures from gold, it must have alloys such as silver or copper added to it. We are like pure gold, created in God's image. But in our humanity alone we are weak, too soft to be of use in His Kingdom. Our trials can make us stronger, more serviceable to Him. He can heal us from our hurts and then use our hurts to make us stronger and help others.

As I write these words, I have recently experienced a series of fiery trials. For almost three months, I was hit with one crisis after another. None of these situations has changed. Relationships are broken, and health is compromised. I have been crushed and depressed, shedding tears at the drop of a hat and not wanting to get out of bed. I took a couple of days to go off by myself and spend time with God. In those precious moments, I prayed, journaled, and cried out to Him. Through the process of being in His presence, I found strength and healing. I'm able to live with the pain of the trials because I know He is with me. I can embrace my trials and still find joy because of Him. Do I still have pain? Of course. But I can endure with joy for God is faithful, and I know He will bring me through. With Job, I can say, "But he knows the way that I take; when he has tested me, I will come forth as gold" (Job 23:10).

Charles Spurgeon is credited with saying, "Fiery trials make golden Christians." How is God using fiery trials to refine you and make you into a "golden Christian?" And how are you learning to embrace your trials so that you can experience joy?

_____

_____

_____

Life has many challenges, Lord, and some of them hurt me deeply. I'm thankful that You can use my trials in my life to refine me like gold, to make me stronger and more productive in Your hands so as to accomplish Your purposes in me. Use my trials to draw me to You, the God Who loves me and always has me in His arms. Amen.

—— DAY 7: REFLECTION AND APPLICATION

My precious Father, I open my heart and mind to You now, as we meet together today. Increase my desire to feed on Your Word and know You more.

Embracing trials with an expectation of joy may seem far-fetched, but it is possible through God's Spirit and power in our lives. Whether you have just gone through a trial or are in one now, God's Word is true and dependable. Our greatest growth and closest intimacy with God through trials is worth it all. As you meditate on what God has revealed to you this week, you may use one of these prompts to guide your reflection.

- In the center of a journal page write a name for a trial you have experienced or are experiencing now, such as "My Divorce." Draw a circle around the name and draw lines that extend out in several directions from the circle. On each line write a result of that trial that turned out to be a benefit for you or others. At the bottom of the journal page write the words of Romans 8:28.

- Write the word *Trials* in a vertical line. Beside each letter write a word or phrase that reflects some aspect of suffering that starts with that letter (e.g., "tense" for the letter T). Try to use words that capture your feelings when you are in a season of trials. At the top, title this acrostic "Feelings from Trials." Make a second vertical line with the word Trials and title this one "Healings from God." Beside each letter write a word or phrase that describes how God works in our lives or provides help during trials (e.g., "trust" for the letter T). Write a reflection of how trials affect you, both negatively and positively, and how your relationship with God is affected by depending on Him through difficult times.

- Locate images of gold items. You may take photos of your own treasured gold possessions. Put these images in your journal and record 1 Peter 1:7 and Job 23:10 on the same page.

- Find a song that encourages you in this process. You may document the lyrics and record your own reflections on them, or you could illustrate them with sketches or images you locate. Two examples for this week's study are "Son of Suffering" by David Funk (2021) and "When Trials Come" by Keith and Kristyn Getty (2009).

Your journal is a very private and personal process; therefore, share it carefully. If social media is a healthy place for you, use these hashtags for posting your words, images, other reflections, or personal stories from this study: #fp4h and #fp4habetterway. You can view my journal and others' entries using these hashtags.

My joy comes only from You, my Lord. Through trials I come to know you more and grow in faith in Your faithfulness. Give me power to embrace my trials as You work in me to change me into all You want me to be. Amen.

1 Lesli White, "4 Amazing Stories of Martyrdom and Costly Discipleship," Beliefnet (2023), https://www.beliefnet.com/faiths/christianity/galleries/4-amazing-stories-of-martyrdom-and-costly-discipleship.aspx.

2 "James 1,"Step Bible (2023), https://www.stepbible.org/?q=version=ESV|reference=-Jas.1&options=NHVUG.

3 Chuck Swindoll, "James," Insight for Living (2023), https://www.insight.org/resources/bible/the-general-epistles/james.

4 Annie Johnson Flint, "He Giveth More Grace," Hymary.org (2022), https://hymnary.org/text/he_giveth_more_grace_as_our_burdens. Public domain.

WEEK EIGHT: SEEK FIRST THE KINGDOM

SCRIPTURE MEMORY VERSE

Therefore, everyone who hears these words of mine and puts them into practice is like a wise man who built his house on the rock. The rain came down, the streams rose, and the winds blew and beat against that house; yet it did not fall, because it had its foundation on the rock. Matthew 7:24-25

Jesus preached a sermon recorded in Matthew 5-7. We call this message the Sermon on the Mount. Our lessons in this study have focused on these challenging teachings as we have reflected on how we can choose God's better way to follow Jesus and live in His upside-down Kingdom, especially as it relates to our battle to consistently make healthy choices. Jesus' words are rock-solid principles that are the foundation for the Kingdom seeker's life.

Last week in *A Better Way*, we learned about embracing suffering to become joyful.

- We can choose joy during trials because God can use them to develop our character.
- Our trials can increase our dependence on God.
- In God's hands, our trials have purposes for His glory and our good.
- Annie Johnson Flint, Paul and Barnabas, the Macedonian Christians, David, and—most of all—Jesus are examples of those who found permanent joy in their trials.
- Eternal glory and joy is forever; our trials are momentary in comparison.

In this final week of *A Better Way*, we will dig into the solid-rock principles that Jesus used to build a strong foundation in our lives. As we practice the words He taught, we become Kingdom seekers who put Him first and love Him with all our heart, soul, mind, and strength.

——— DAY 1: THE SOLID ROCK

Take my hand today, God, and guide me into all things. Speak to me as I open Your Word and search for Your truth.

During the last seven weeks, we have considered God's better way to live in Jesus' upside-down Kingdom. Here are the aspects of Kingdom-living that we explored.

- Lose your life to find it
- Be weak to become strong
- Give away to receive
- Be hungry to become satisfied
- Serve to be honored
- Walk by faith instead of sight
- Embrace trials to become joyful

We do not develop these mindsets and traits on our own. They are cultivated through Christ's work in us and take a lifetime to perfect. These Kingdom seeker characteristics are built on a foundation. Record this week's memory verses here.

_____

_____

_____

Read Matthew 7:24-27. Jesus says we are like a wise man if we do what?

_____

_____

_____

Home builders know that there are specific steps required to construct a house's concrete foundation. They must draw blueprints, prepare the land, install the footings, build the forms, set the rebar, and pour the concrete. If someone listened to the experts then decided to build a foundation his own way, he is hearing but not doing. When it comes to laying a strong foundation in a Kingdom seeker, Jesus says we must "hear" His Word and then "put it into practice." The foolish person does the opposite. He hears God's Word but doesn't apply it into his daily life.

Look up James 1:22-25. What are we encouraged to do?

_____

_____

_____

How does studying God's Word resemble a mirror in your life?

_____

_____

_____

What does Paul tell us is the foundation of our faith in 1 Corinthians 3:11?

_____

This week we will examine some important parts of the foundation Jesus wants to build in His Kingdom seekers. He gives us His Word and invites us to partner with Him in developing a strong basis for our life with Him.

Thank You for building a strong foundation in me, God. I want to be like the wise man and not the foolish man. Teach me how to hear Your Word and put it into practice every day as I seek You and Your Kingdom first. Amen.

—— DAY 2: PRAYER

Here I am in Your holy presence, Lord, bringing all my problems and praises. I trust You to pour out Your Spirit in me anew so that I can hear Your voice and learn Your ways.

One important part of our foundation in Christ is prayer. There are countless books, sermons, and workshops on prayer. But the most important way to learn about prayer is to pray. Talking to God is an amazing privilege we have, made possible by Jesus' sacrifice. Today let's explore some elements of prayer as He taught us, but let's practice praying at the same time.

Read Mark 11:24. What is one essential element of prayer according to Jesus?

_____

_____

_____

Write a prayer to God, expressing your faith in Him.

_____

_____

_____

A second teaching related to prayer is found in John 14:13-15. Why is verse 15 important to understand the teaching of verses 13 and 14?

_____

_____

_____

Write a prayer expressing your allegiance to God and commitment to fully obey Him.

_____

_____

_____

Let's look at a third part of the prayer foundation. Find Matthew 6:12 (part of the Lord's Prayer) and Matthew 5:23-24. On what aspect of prayer does Jesus focus?

_____

_____

_____

Confess any sins God brings to your mind, and ask for and receive His forgiveness.

_____

_____

_____

_____

The next essential element concerns our motives for praying to God. Re-read John 14:13-14. How does James 4:2-3 help us understand the importance of having right motives for prayer?

_____

_____

_____

Write a prayer that reflects an expression about your desire for His Kingdom's sake and not selfish desires.

_____

_____

_____

Look back at what you have written and combine your prayer statements into one prayer. End it with an expression of thanksgiving for God's faithfulness in answering your prayers (1 Thessalonians 5:18).

_____

_____

_____

_____

_____

Additional teachings of Jesus about prayer are found in Matthew 6:5-8 and Luke 11:5-8. Summarize these teachings on prayer.

_____

_____

How do your prayers reflect authenticity, intimacy with God, and persistence?

_____

_____

Finally, what do we expect to happen as a result of our prayers? We've read that Jesus said if we ask in His Name, we will receive. But sometimes what we receive is not what we expect. Read about Paul's experience in 2 Corinthians 12:7-10. How did God answer his prayer and why did He answer in that way?

_____

_____

In the upside-down Kingdom of God, sometimes He gives us exactly what we ask for in prayer, and sometimes He gives us something different. But we can be certain that His answer is always best for us and for His Kingdom's purposes. How did Jesus describe this in Luke 11:11-13?

_____

_____

_____

We have identified these essential elements of prayer.
- Faith
- Obedience
- Forgiveness
- In His Name with pure motives
- Thanksgiving
- Authenticity, intimacy with God, and persistence
- The goodness of God's answers

In Mark 1:35, we read, "Very early in the morning, while it was still dark, Jesus got up, left the house and went off to a solitary place, where he prayed." Prayer was a priority and practice for Jesus. The One Who knows God best and is joined with Him in the Holy Trinity craved conversation with Him. He modeled the importance of prayer for His followers, a vital part of the foundation of living as a Kingdom seeker.

Thank You for always hearing me, God, and help me to practice prayer daily using these essential elements that Jesus taught us. Remind me throughout the day that I can come to You anytime and talk with You, my good and faithful Father. Amen.

—— DAY 3: THE WORD
As I come into Your presence now, Lord, I seek Your face. For only in You can I find all I need.

God's Word is a central part of the First Place for Health program. We read the Bible daily, and some of us strive to read the whole Bible through in a year. We dig into it daily in our Bible studies and discuss it at our weekly meetings. We memorize and recite scriptures weekly as well. We believe it is part of the foundation of following Jesus and making healthy choices. Write this week's memory verses here.

_____

_____

Why is God's Word so important and how does it serve as a part of the solid foundation Jesus taught at the end of the Sermon on the Mount?

_____

_____

_____

Let's find out what Jesus said about His Word as well as the Word of God. Read Matthew 24:35; what quality about His words did Jesus identify?

_____

_____

_____

First, God's Word is *eternal*. It is part of a strong foundation because it will never disappear. We can stand firmly on God's Word, which grounds us in a world that is constantly changing and redefining good and evil on its own terms. Next look up Matthew 4:4. What does Jesus say about God's Word in this verse?

_____

_____

_____

Second, God's Word is *essential*. We cannot live without it. Our daily and weekly practices of engaging in God's Word give us spiritual nourishment that Kingdom seekers need to survive in this broken world. Now find John 8:31-32. What does Jesus say is the result of following His teaching?

_____

_____

_____

Third, God's Word is *emancipating*. When I live by God's Word, I am free in Christ, no longer bound to the cruel slavery of sin and selfishness. I am living for Him and not for myself. I am focused on His Kingdom's purposes.

Other New Testament authors wrote about the importance of God's Word. Remember that the only written Bible they had at the time was the Old Testament or Hebrew Bible. Read each passage and record what it says about God's Word.

Scripture	What It Says about God's Word
Romans 15:4	
2 Timothy 3:16-17	
Hebrews 4:12	

How do these qualities of God's Word impact you as you read, study, and memorize it?

_____

_____

_____

Since I joined First Place for Health in the fall of 1981, I have read the Bible through every year. I have found His Word to be everything we've studied today and more. Sometimes parts of the Old Testament may be dry or confusing. Yet God continues to show me truth in His Word that is relevant and vital to my walk with Christ. His Word constantly challenges and changes me as nothing else can. Showing up daily to read His Word represents our allegiance to Him and desire to know Him more.

There is a beautiful passage in Isaiah that expresses the power and purpose of God's Word. Read Isaiah 55:10-12. What imagery does Isaiah use in verse 10 to describe God's Word?

_____

_____

_____

What does verse 11 say about the purpose of God's Word?

_____

_____

_____

What is the result of God's Word in verse 12?

_____

_____

_____

How is God's Word a part of your daily focus?

_____

_____

_____

How would you like to make God's Word more a part of your life?

_____

_____

_____

Is there a time in your life or the life of someone you know where God's Word was evident, accomplishing something that was undeniably His work? If so, describe it here.

_____

_____

_____

Our foundation in Christ is God's Word, which is Christ Himself (John 1:1-2). Let us implement His Word in our lives daily, for it is a lamp unto our feet and a light unto our paths (Psalm 119:105).

Thank You for Your Word, Father, for it is my nourishment, my strength, and my help. You have freed me through Your truths and give me direction through Your teachings. Encourage me as I seek to follow Your Word with all my being. Amen.

—— DAY 4: FELLOWSHIP

My heart and mind turn to You, Father, as I enter into this quiet time. As I bow before You and open Your Word, give me wisdom and understanding.

When you hear the word *fellowship*, what images come to your mind? In the church where I grew up, that word meant a gathering with food, laughter, music, and socializing. I feel warm inside as I remember all the good times we had at church fellowships. But fellowship is much more than an event. It involves *relationships* with other believers that grow deeper over time. As a pillar of our foundation in Christ, fellowship with other believers gives us support as we live in His Kingdom here on earth.

The early church modeled this community mindset in several ways. Read Acts 2:42-47 and describe what early church members did.

_____

_____

_____

The word translated *fellowship* is the Greek word *koinonia*. It involves the close association between people, emphasizing what they have in common.[1] Notice in verse 42 that the early church members devoted themselves to fellowship. They were hyper-focused on their relationships with each other because of their new lives in Christ. Fellowship was a priority. Jesus Himself built relationships with people and practiced community and fellowship with His followers. What are we encouraged to do in Hebrews 10:24-25?

_____

_____

_____

During the COVID pandemic that started in 2020, we experienced quarantine and isolation. We learned how much we need each other. Although we stayed connected by using technology, it was not the same as meeting in person and having physical contact. More than ever, we discovered personal connections and fellowship are critical to our walk with Christ and our mental and emotional health. This need is why our First Place for Health meetings are so important. When possible, our face-to-face interactions with others who are focused on a similar goal give us accountability, strength, and opportunities to minister to each other. Our fellowship supports our foundation and helps keep it sturdy.

Jesus taught His followers an important truth about our fellowship. What did He say in Matthew 18:19-20?

_____

_____

_____

Paul describes fellowship in Philippians 2:1-4. What does he encourage us to do in our relationship to others?

_____

_____

In Galatians 6:2 what are we encouraged to do?

_____

_____

_____

What is "the law of Christ?" (See Matthew 22:39.)

_____

_____

_____

Finally read 1 John 1:3-7 and 1 John 4:11-12. What do these verses teach about fellowship?

_____

_____

_____

Some may struggle with attending weekly meetings due to various conflicts. There may be times we don't want to go because we are not feeling successful. But the gathering of like-minded believers is one of the most powerful sources of spiritual strength available to us on earth. We can persistently set that time aside each week, arrive on time, pray for our leader and group members, be mentally present, and participate fully in what God is doing among our group—even if we are meeting in a virtual setting. It is part of the strong foundation of Kingdom living. How does your First Place for Health group support you and how do you support it?

_____

_____

_____

Thank You for my First Place for Health leader and group members, Lord. I appreciate our relationships and am eager to support them as they support me on my wellness journey and walk with You. Use our meetings and interactions to keep us strong in Your Kingdom's work. Amen.

—— DAY 5: COUNTING THE COST

Your Kingdom come, O Lord. Your will be done on earth as it is in heaven. Teach me today about living in Your Kingdom here on earth.

Many people from other countries see America as a land of great opportunity. Through the centuries immigrants have sacrificed a great deal to come to the United States in hopes of finding a better life. My mother-in-law said her grandmother came to the U.S. from Europe, crossing an ocean alone at age 16, not knowing what the future held for her. She paid a price to find a new life.

Jesus encouraged his followers to be aware of the cost of following Him. Read Luke 14:25-33. In verse 26 what does Jesus say His disciples must do?

_____

_____

_____

Does Jesus mean we should literally hate our family members as a prerequisite to following Him? No, it is an example of hyperbole, which Jesus often used in His teachings—emphasizing the seriousness of becoming His disciple. What else does He say is involved in verse 27?

_____

_____

_____

We already looked at the idea of carrying His cross on Day 4 of Week 1 of this study. It is central to the mindset of a Kingdom seeker. Jesus gives two examples of counting the cost in verses 28-32. What are they?

_____

_____

_____

What is the challenge Jesus ends with in verse 33?

_____

_____

_____

What is the cost of following Jesus and living in His Kingdom? *Everything*. Nothing held back. All in. One hundred percent. Hands off anything I own or think is mine. Laser focused on His Kingdom and not me. All or nothing. Declaring, "I'm yours at any cost."[2] Total allegiance to Jesus and willing to do anything He asks. Becoming the person whose characteristics are described in the Beatitudes. Giving up everything you cherish, even your own life. Passionately seeking His Kingdom first.

When I think about my eating and exercise choices in this context, it means that I don't get to pick what I eat. I have put all my own desires aside and follow only what Jesus tells me to do. I don't do it perfectly, but it is my commitment to do my best as I seek Him first. Many times I hear my First Place for Health group members say they need to "get back on the (food) plan." We don't get "on the plan" in God's Kingdom. God gets in us and does His will in us to make healthy choices and obey His will. And He does that through our complete faith in Him, totally committed to Him in every way. As Jesus faced His cross of suffering and death, He said, "Father, remove this cup from me. But please, not what I want. What do you want?" (Luke 22:42 MSG)

Here are questions we can ask ourselves. What does God want from me? Have I held anything back from full surrender to Him? What do I need to relinquish in my life to ensure I am all in with Him? How would you answer these questions?

_____

_____

_____

In Mark 10:28 Peter said that he and the other disciples had left everything to follow Christ. He seemed to want Jesus to recognize their level of sacrifice and get a gold star for their commitment. But Jesus challenged him, saying that leaving everything was for Him and the sake of the gospel, not personal achievement or a place of honor in God's Kingdom. Instead, "many who are first will be last, and the last first" (verse 31). In this vein Oswald Chambers encourages us to search our hearts carefully to ensure we are totally sold out to Christ.

Beware of surrender that is motivated by personal benefits that may result. For example, "I'm going to give myself to God because I want to be delivered from sin, because I want to be made holy." Being delivered from sin and being made holy are the result of being right with God, but surrender resulting from this kind of thinking is certainly not the true nature of Christianity.[3]

How does this challenge to give up everything for Jesus and the gospel impact your motives for making healthy choices?

_____

_____

_____

The cost of following You is enormous, God. It means everything I am and have are Yours, not mine. Give me wisdom and courage to release all my self-centered attitudes and my devotion to anything other than You. I want to seek You and Your Kingdom above anything else. Amen

—— DAY 6: REFLECTION AND APPLICATION

O Lord, my God, how glorious is Your Name in all the heavens and earth! I praise You for Your majesty and power, for Your steadfast love and faithfulness. My heart longs for You and Your righteousness.

Yesterday we examined the cost of being a Kingdom seeker. Today we'll look at the rewards of Kingdom living. The gospel accounts record Jesus mentioning the Kingdom of God or Kingdom of heaven over 120 times. It appears thirty-four times through- out the rest of the New Testament and was a focus of His ministry and of the Bible authors' writings. Although the cost of being a Kingdom seeker is high, the rewards are amazing. In fact, in the Beatitudes Jesus tells us how blessed we are when we live as His followers. We have reviewed many of these benefits throughout this study. Here are a few of them.

- Forgiveness for all sin
- Friendship with Jesus, our Advocate and High Priest
- Indwelling and guidance of the Holy Spirit
- Inner peace, contentment, and freedom regardless of circumstances
- Power to overcome temptation and evil
- Protection and presence of God
- Access to God's throne where we can ask for anything in His Name
- Discernment and wisdom
- Fruit of the Spirit
- Persistence and hope in difficult time
- Purpose for living
- Forever home in heaven

Which of these benefits is most important to you at this time of your life? Why?

_____

_____

_____

In the Lord's Prayer Jesus taught us to ask God that His kingdom would come (Matthew 6:10). He was asking that God would continue to bring about the salvation of every person and give them life in the midst of a dark and dying world. From the beginning of time, the Lord has been on a passionate quest to rescue you and make you His own. The Kingdom of God is the best place you can reside as a citizen. What does this truth mean to you?

_____

_____

_____

At the beginning of this study, we considered the movie *The Matrix*. The protagonist, Thomas Anderson, discovered he was living in a fake world, that the real world was being hidden from him. Perhaps the Kingdom of God is not the upside-world we think it is. Maybe this earthly world is upside-down, the world that feeds us lies and calls us away from our loving heavenly Father. God's better way might be the true way of life and not the upside-down lifestyle the world teaches us to reject. Finding God through Jesus is the way we break free from the false existence of earth and become the inhabitants of the real world, which is the Kingdom of God.

As you reflect on how God has worked in you during this study and this session of First Place for Health, what comes to mind? How has He been leading you in His Word and through prayer to embrace and pursue this Kingdom lifestyle?

_____

_____

_____

What obstacles have you faced?

_____

_____

_____

What victories have you won?

_____

_____

_____

What do you want God to do next as you continue to seek Him and His Kingdom first?

_____

_____

_____

Let us join together as Kingdom people and pray a prayer based on Ephesians 3:14-21.

We kneel before You, our Father, from whom every family in heaven and on earth derives its name. We pray that out of Your glorious riches that You strengthen us with power through Your Spirit in our inner beings, so that Christ may dwell in our hearts through faith. And we pray that we, being rooted and established in love, have power, together with all Your holy people, to grasp how wide and long and high and deep is the love of Christ and to know this love that surpasses the world's upside-down knowledge—that we may be filled to the measure of all the fullness of God. Now to Him Who is able to do immeasurably more than all we ask or imagine, according to His power that is at work within us, to Him be glory in the church and in Christ Jesus throughout all generations, for ever and ever! Amen.

Thank You for the truth of Your Kingdom, Lord, the place of my real citizenship and where I find You. You are continuing to do a good work in me, God, for Your Kingdom's sake, and I ask You to lead me in Your ways as I seek You first in all things. I love You, Lord. Amen.

—— DAY 7: REFLECTION AND APPLICATION

You are my Savior and my Lord, my one and only source of life and strength. During this quiet time, speak to my heart and fill me with all of You.

We have come to the end of this study, *A Better Way.* Jesus' teachings have challenged us to live in a radically different way than the lifestyle of the world. How have these teachings encouraged you in your wellness journey? What has God done in your life to bring about a Kingdom mindset as you seek Him first in all things and love Him with all your being? Use today's quiet time to reflect on these questions and all that God is currently doing in and through you. Here are some prompts that may help your reflection process and spark your journaling. Choose one for today's meditation.

- Divide your journal page into eight equal parts. At the top of each section write one of the titles of the eight weeks of study (See the list of 1-7 on Day 1 of this week's lesson). In each section write something you believe about that part of living in God's Kingdom based on what you've learned during this study. You can use words and/or images and/or scripture references.

- Write "God's Word" in the center of your journal page. Draw lines from those words toward the edges of the page. On each line write a scripture that expresses some characteristic of God's Word. Some scriptures are in Day 3 of this week's lesson; you can use those and/or add others.

- Write "Kingdom Seeking" at the top of your journal page. Draw a vertical line down the middle of the rest of the page. Write "Costs" on the top of the left column and "Benefits" at the top of the right column. Lists the costs and benefits we looked during Day 5 and 6 this week, and add any additional ones you'd like. At the bottom write a prayer thanking God for providing a way for you to live as a Kingdom seeker in His forever Kingdom.

- Find a song that encourages you in this process. You may document the lyrics and record your own reflections on them, or you could illustrate them with sketches or images you locate. Two examples for this week's study are "Firm Foundation (He Won't)" by Carnes, Davis, and Moore (2021) and "Kingdom Come" by Covenant Worship (2014).

Your journal is a very private and personal process; therefore, share it carefully. If social media is a healthy place for you, use these hashtags for posting your words, images, other reflections, or personal stories from this study: #fp4h and #fp4habetterway. You can view my journal and others' entries using these hashtags.

Thank You for this session of First Place for Health and for all the ways You have changed me. I appreciate all the members and the leader of my group, and I pray we will continue to seek You and Your Kingdom's better way above all things as we strive to live healthier lives. Without You we are nothing, Lord. But with You we have the victory through Jesus Christ our Lord. I love You. Amen.

1 Acts 2. Step Bible (2023), https://www.stepbible.org/?q=version=ESV|refer-
ence=Acts.2&options=HNVUG.
2 John Piper, "Following Christ Is Costly—But How Do You Count the Cost?" Desiring
God (2018), https://www.desiringgod.org/interviews/following-christ-is-costly-but-how-
do-you-count-the-cost.
3 Oswald Chambers, "Total Surrender," My Utmost for His Highest (2023), https://
utmost.org/total-surrender/.

WEEK NINE: A TIME TO CELEBRATE

This study has provided opportunities to learn about God's better way in the upside-down world system of earth. To help you shape your short victory celebration testimony, work through the following questions in your prayer journal, one on each day leading up to your group's celebration.

DAY ONE: List some of the benefits you have gained by allowing the Lord to transform your life through this First Place for Health session. Be mindful that He has been active in all four aspects of your being, so list benefits you have received in the physical, mental, emotional and spiritual realms.

DAY TWO: In what ways have you most significantly changed mentally? Have you seen a shift in the ways you think about yourself, food, your relationships, or God? How has Scripture memory been a part of these shifts?

DAY THREE: In what ways have you most significantly changed emotionally? Have you begun to identify how your feelings influence your relationship to food and exercise? What are you doing to stay aware of your emotions, both positive and negative?

DAY FOUR: In what ways have you most significantly changed spiritually? How has your relationship with God deepened? How has drawing closer to Him made a difference in the other three areas of your life?

DAY FIVE: In what ways have you most significantly changed physically? Have you met or exceeded your weight/measurement goals? How has your health improved during the past twelve weeks?

DAY SIX: Was there one person in your First Place for Health group who was particularly encouraging to you? How did their kindness make a difference in your First Place for Health journey?

DAY SEVEN: Summarize the previous six questions into a one-page testimony, or "faith story," to share at your group's victory celebration.

May our Mighty God make you victorious in Him, as you continue to keep Him first in all things!

LEADER DISCUSSION GUIDE

For in-depth information, guidance and helpful tips about leading a successful First Place for Health group, spend time studying the *My Place for Leadership* book. In it, you will find valuable answers to most of your questions, as well as personal insights from many First Place for Health group leaders.

For the group meetings in this session, be sure to read and consider each week's discussion topics several days before the meeting—some questions and activities require supplies and/or planning to complete. Also, if you are leading a large group, plan to break into smaller groups for discussion and then come together as a large group to share your answers and responses. Make sure to appoint a capable leader for each small group so that discussions stay focused and on track (and be sure each group records their answers!).

——WEEK ONE: LOSE YOUR LIFE TO FIND IT

1. As you begin this first lesson of this session, encourage your members to participate and ask questions during the discussion. You may start with an open-ended question such as, "What do you think the title of this Bible study tells us about what we will be studying?"

2. How did Jesus model dying to live? How does His example of giving up our lives to find them impact our daily walk?

3. Read about the heart swap idea shared from Max Lucado. How does this idea of swapping your heart for Jesus' heart fit into your idea of salvation? How has Jesus changed your heart since you first accepted His gift of eternal life?

4. Review this week's memory verse. Discuss this statement from Day 3: "Our food and exercise choices can be worshipful experiences because we are sacrificing our own desires to God."

5. Discuss Galatians 2:19-20 and what it means to live a crucified life. What desires do you have that you need to crucify and leave behind?

6. Look over the chart in Day 5 and examine how these Biblical truths are related to developing healthy habits. Is there any part of your life that has a No Trespassing sign on it?

7. Encourage members to share any journaling they did during the week if they feel comfortable doing so. You might split the group up into pairs or small groups for journal and reflection sharing.

——— WEEK TWO: BE WEAK TO BECOME STRONG

1. Review the Week 1 summary at the beginning of the Week 2 lesson.
2. Share what you originally thought about the word meekness as used in the Beatitudes and what you learned or had confirmed in this lesson.
3. Review the ways Jesus modeled meekness in the Day 1 lesson. How is His example different from what we see in the world? In the church? In our own lives?
4. Discuss how we gain strength from love and the Holy Spirit. How do these reflect a lifestyle of Christ-like meekness?
5. Read John 1:14 and talk about how Jesus tabernacles with us. How does Paul's experience in 2 Corinthians 12:9-10 impact your understanding of God's work in your life through your weakness?
6. Briefly review the story of the Israelites at the Red Sea and God's direction for them to stand still. How has God used this discipline of standing still while He works in your life? Why is it hard to be still and wait for God?
7. Recite this week's memory verse as a group. Express your thoughts about this statement from Day 5: "Cultivating meekness means we understand that we are right where God wants us to be."
8. Review the chart from Day 6 and ask volunteers to share what they wrote down.
9. Encourage members to share any journaling they did during the week if they feel comfortable doing so. You might split the group up into pairs or small groups for journal and reflection sharing.

——— WEEK THREE: GIVE AWAY TO RECEIVE

1. Review the Week 2 summary at the beginning of the Week 3 lesson.
2. What is your most prized possession? Why?
3. What does the concept of storing up treasures on earth look like for you?
4. Discuss the idea of "stinkin' thinkin'" and ask members to share anything they identified that fits this category.
5. Read Matthew 19:16-21 (including this week's memory verse). What might Jesus ask you to leave behind to follow Him?
6. Review the excerpt by Tara-Leigh Cobble from Day 3 and ask members to share how God has provided for their needs in the past.
7. The topic from Day 4 is accountability. What accountability measures do you currently have in place and what measures would you like to add to your practices?
8. Let's talk about attitudes about food choices. Are you grateful about making

healthy choices or are you grumbling? How can God help you change your attitude if it needs to be changed?

9. Share how you practiced giving away this past week. How did it impact your healthy habits? If you didn't practice giving away, how could you do that this week? How does giving away allow you to receive God's best for them?

10. Encourage members to share any journaling they did during the week if they feel comfortable doing so. You might split the group up into pairs or small groups for journal and reflection sharing.

—— WEEK FOUR: BE HUNGRY TO BECOME SATISFIED

1. Review the Week 3 summary at the beginning of the Week 4 lesson.

2. Share an experience in your life when you were the most satisfied. What made it satisfying? What does that tell you about yourself?

3. Let's discuss the word righteousness and this quote: "Righteousness is less about evaluating my behavior and more about developing a faithful relationship with God."

4. Pose the question from Day 2: "What would my life look like if I hungered for God as much as or more than I hunger for food?" How can we become hungrier for Him?

5. Review these scripture passages from Day 3: Psalm 40:8, Ephesians 4:22-24, and 2 Timothy 3:16-17. How does reading and studying God's Word affect the way you think and your self-talk?

6. Reflect on the challenges associated with emotional eating. What causes you to eat based on your emotions? How have you succeeded in overcoming emotional eating? What do you need to conquer or maintain victory over emotional eating?

7. Look back at the practical ways we can empty ourselves from Day 5. Which one of these methods have you implemented? How did it impact you? What would you like to try next?

8. Ask members to choose one of the four parts of our being: emotional, spiritual, mental, and physical. If you meet face-to-face, designate each corner of the room as one of the four parts, and tell members to go to the corner of the room that represents the part of their being that they chose. If you meet virtually, divide members into breakout rooms. As they meet in their small groups, tell members to talk about why they chose that part of their being and what they want God to do to help them with it. The groups can close in prayer.

9. How did you respond to Dietrich Bonhoeffer's writing from Day 6?

0. Encourage members to share any journaling they did during the week if they feel comfortable doing so. You might split the group up into pairs or small groups for journal and reflection sharing.

—— WEEK FIVE: SERVE TO BE HONORED

. Review the Week 4 summary at the beginning of the Week 5 lesson.

2. What does service in God's Kingdom look like to you? How did Jesus model this service for us?

3. How does it feel when someone serves you? How does it feel when you serve someone else?

4. Review the characteristics of a servant's heart from Day 2: sacrificial, devoted, and humble. What are some ways you see members of our group exemplify these attributes?

5. Day 3 identifies three groups we can serve: other Christians, those in need, and our enemies. Discuss ways you already serve these groups and ways you can serve them in the future.

6. Let's discuss the importance of prayer in serving others. How does prayer represent what Jesus taught about servanthood?

7. How has being a part of First Place for Health given you opportunities to share the gospel? How could God use your desire to put Him first in all things and love Him with your whole being as a way to witness to people in your life?

8. Review the scripture passages from Day 5 that can inspire us to love and serve. How did these verses impact your motivation to serve God and others?

9. Ask for volunteers to share the responses to the Day 6 questions about their service involving their talents and gifts and their service that is outside their comfort zones. If there is an opportunity for your group to serve together in your church or in the community at large, ask for volunteers to plan and carry out a service project.

10. Encourage members to share any journaling they did during the week if they feel comfortable doing so. You might split the group up into pairs or small groups for journal and reflection sharing.

—— WEEK SIX: WALK BY FAITH INSTEAD OF SIGHT

1. Review the Week 5 summary at the beginning of the Week 6 lesson.

2. Look at the stories from Day 1 about Bartimaeus and Thomas. How do you use your faith to make decisions even when your senses may be in conflict with your faith?

3. When did you experience a time in your life when God accomplished an impossible feat that only He could do?
4. How does God's Word impact your "faith sense?" What is a favorite verse that encourages you to believe in God even when things look hopeless?
5. Call on a volunteer to read or summarize Acts 16:25-34. How did God work through Paul and Silas' faith? Why is faith essential during difficult times?
6. Review the practical applications listed at the end of Day 3. What do these activities look like in your life? Share any additional ways God leads you to engage your faith in your daily life.
7. Let's discuss the connection between faith and obedience. What challenges do you face to be obedient to God's Word and His work in you? How has He helped you overcome reluctance to obey Him?
8. When did God has asked you to take a leap of faith? Did you do it? What was the result? What are the risks of taking a leap of faith? What are the rewards?
9. How do the Holy Spirit and other First Place for Health members encourage you in your faith and support you in trusting God above all things?
10. Encourage members to share any journaling they did during the week if they feel comfortable doing so. You might split the group up into pairs or small groups for journal and reflection sharing.

—— WEEK SEVEN: EMBRACE TRIALS TO BECOME JOYFUL

1. Review the Week 6 summary at the beginning of the Week 7 lesson.
2. Recite this week's memory verses together. Review the meaning the three words listed in Day 1. How does knowing these deeper meanings of these words expand your understanding of this scripture passage?
3. Recruit a volunteer to read 1 Peter 1:6-7. How do these verses encourage us to remain joyful even in the midst of suffering?
4. When are you the most dependent on God? Why do you think that is true for you?
5. What purposes for suffering did you identify in the Day 3 lesson? How does understanding a purpose in difficult times impact our response to them? What do you do if you can't find a purpose in suffering?
6. Ask a member to read John 15:1-5. Describe how this metaphor relates to you.
7. Review Hebrews 12:1-3. What was "the joy set before Him (Jesus)?" How does this compare to the joy you can find during painful experiences?
8. Matthew 5:11-12 says that we are blessed when we are persecuted. Have you ever been persecuted for your faith in Jesus? If so, what happened and how did you respond?

9. How does focusing on our eternal home with God encourage you and give you joy even when earthly life seems unbearable?
10. Encourage members to share any journaling they did during the week if they feel comfortable doing so. You might split the group up into pairs or small groups for journal and reflection sharing.

— WEEK EIGHT: SEEK FIRST THE KINGDOM

1. Review the Week 7 summary at the beginning of the Week 8 lesson.
2. Ask a volunteer to read Matthew 7:24-29. How does following Jesus' teachings create a firm foundation in our lives?
3. Encourage members to share the prayers they wrote in the Day 2 lesson. Discuss how we pray, the challenges we face, and how God uses prayer to keep us grounded in our obedience to Him.
4. How is God's Word eternal, essential, and emancipating? How does God's Word play a part in your life in practical ways?
5. Read Isaiah 55:10-12. What do these verses say to you about God's Word?
6. What does the word fellowship mean to you in the context of Christian community? How has fellowship impacted your daily walk with Christ?
7. What costs have you paid or do you pay in order to follow Jesus? What do you give up as a part of practicing healthy habits in First Place for Health? Why do you do it?
8. Discuss this excerpt from the Day 5 lesson: "We don't get 'on the plan' in God's Kingdom. God gets in us and does His will in us to make healthy choices and obey His will."
9. What does seeking God and His Kingdom first mean to you? How does making healthy choices reflect your complete allegiance to God?
10. Encourage members to share any journaling they did during the week if they feel comfortable doing so. You might split the group up into pairs or small groups for journal and reflection sharing.

— WEEK NINE: TIME TO CELEBRATE

s your class members reflect on each week's content, help them remember the ays God has taught them about His better way. Ask: How has God empowered u to choose His better way and live in His Kingdom rather than the world?

FIRST PLACE FOR HEALTH
JUMP START MENUS

All recipe and menu nutritional information was determined using the Master-Cook software, a program that accesses a database containing more than 6,000 food items prepared using the United States Department of Agriculture (USDA) publications and information from food manufacturers.

As with any nutritional program, MasterCook calculates the nutritional values of the recipes based on ingredients. Nutrition may vary due to how the food is prepared, where the food comes from, soil content, season, ripeness, processing and method of preparation. You are expected to add snacks and sides as needed to meet your nutritional needs. For these reasons, please use the recipes and menu plans as approximate guides. As always, consult your physician and/or a registered dietitian before starting a weight-loss program.

Lemon Parfait

2 cups reduced-fat plain Greek yogurt
1/4 cup honey
2 tablespoons lemon juice
2 teaspoons grated lemon zest
2 tablespoons chia seeds
1 teaspoon vanilla extract
1 cup fresh raspberries
1 cup fresh blueberries

Combine the first 6 ingredients. Layer half the yogurt mixture into 4 small parfait glasses or custard cups. Top with half the berries. Repeat layers. Serves 1

Nutritional Information: 214 calories, 4g fat, 7mg cholesterol, 33g carbohydrate, 13g protein, 48mg sodium

Chicken Cucumber Boats

2 medium cucumbers
1/2 cup fat-free plain Greek yogurt
2 tablespoons mayonnaise
1/2 teaspoon garlic salt
3 teaspoons snipped fresh dill, divided
1 cup chopped cooked chicken breast
1 cup chopped seeded tomato (about 1 large), divided
1/2 cup fresh or frozen peas, thawed

Cut each cucumber lengthwise in half; scoop out pulp, leaving a 1/4-in. shell. In a bowl, mix yogurt, mayonnaise, garlic salt and 1 teaspoon dill; gently stir in chicken, 3/4 cup tomato and peas. Spoon into cucumber shells. Top with the remaining tomato and dill. Serves 2

Nutritional Information: 2 filled cucumber halves: 312 calories, 12g fat, 55mg cholesterol, 18g carbohydrate, 34g protein, 641mg sodium

DAY 1 | DINNER

One Pan Chicken and Vegetables

2 pounds red potatoes, cut into 3/4-inch pieces
1 large onion, coarsely chopped
2 tablespoons olive oil
3 garlic cloves, minced
1-1/4 teaspoons salt, divided
1 teaspoon dried rosemary, crushed, divided
3/4 teaspoon pepper, divided
1/2 teaspoon paprika
6 bone-in chicken thighs (about 2-1/4 pounds), skin removed
6 cups fresh baby spinach (about 6 ounces)
Lemon wedges, optional

Preheat oven to 425°. In a large bowl, combine potatoes, onion, oil, garlic, 3/4 tea-spoon salt, 2 teaspoons fresh rosemary or 1/2 teaspoon dried rosemary, and 1/2 tea-spoon pepper; toss to coat. Transfer to a 15x10x1-in. baking pan coated with cooking spray. In a small bowl, mix paprika and the remaining salt, rosemary and pepper. Sprin-kle chicken with paprika mixture; arrange over vegetables. Roast until a thermometer inserted in chicken reads 170°-175° and vegetables are just tender, 35-40 minutes. Remove chicken to a serving platter; keep warm. Top vegetables with spinach. Roast until vegetables are tender and spinach is wilted, 8-10 minutes longer. Stir vegetables to combine; serve with chicken. If desired, serve with lemon wedges. Serves 6

Nutritional Information: 1 chicken thigh with 1 cup vegetables: 357 calories, 14g fat, 87mg cholesterol, 28g carbohydrate, 28g protein, 597mg sodium

DAY 2 | BREAKFAST

Fruity Baked Oatmeal

3 cups quick-cooking oats
1 cup packed brown sugar
2 teaspoons baking powder
1 teaspoon salt
1/2 teaspoon ground cinnamon
2 large eggs, lightly beaten
1 cup fat-free milk
1/2 cup butter, melted
3/4 cup chopped peeled tart apple
1/3 cup chopped fresh or frozen peaches
1/3 cup fresh or frozen blueberries

Preheat oven to 350°. In a large bowl, combine oats, brown sugar, baking powder, salt and cinnamon. Combine eggs, milk and butter; add to the dry ingredients. Stir in apple, peaches and blueberries. Pour into an 8-in. square baking dish coated with cooking spray. Bake, uncovered, until a knife inserted in center comes out clean, 35-40 minutes. Cut into squares. Serve with milk if desired. Serves 9

Nutrition Facts: 1 piece: 322 calories, 13g fat, 75mg cholesterol, 46g carbohydrate, 7g protein, 492mg sodium

Spicy Beef Lettuce Wraps

1 tablespoon canola oil
1 pound lean ground turkey
1 jalapeno pepper, seeded and minced
2 green onions, thinly sliced
2 garlic cloves, minced
2 tablespoons minced fresh basil
2 tablespoons lime juice
2 tablespoons reduced-sodium soy sauce
1 to 2 tablespoons chili garlic sauce
1 tablespoon sugar
12 Boston lettuce leaves
1 medium cucumber, julienned
1 medium carrot, julienned
2 cups bean sprouts

In a large skillet, heat oil over medium heat. Add turkey; cook 6-8 minutes or until no longer pink, breaking into crumbles. Add jalapeno, green onions and garlic; cook 2 minutes longer. Stir in basil, lime juice, soy sauce, chili garlic sauce and sugar; heat through. To serve, place turkey mixture in lettuce leaves; top with cucumber, carrot and bean sprouts. Fold lettuce over filling.

Nutritional Information: 3 lettuce wraps: 259 calories, 12g fat, 78mg cholesterol, 12g carbohydrate, 26g protein, 503mg sodium,

Vegetable Sloppy Joes

8 bacon strips, cut into 1-inch pieces
2 pounds lean ground beef (90% lean)
1 medium onion, chopped
2 garlic cloves, minced
2 cups shredded peeled butternut squash
2 medium parsnips, peeled and shredded
2 medium carrots, peeled and shredded
12 ounces cola
1 8-ounce can tomato paste
1 cup water
1/3 cup honey mustard
1-1/2 teaspoons ground cumin
1-1/4 teaspoons salt
1 teaspoon ground allspice
1/2 teaspoon pepper
18 hamburger buns, split

In large stockpot, cook bacon over medium heat until crisp, stirring occasionally. Remove with a slotted spoon; drain on paper towels. Discard drippings. In the same skillet, cook beef, onion and garlic over medium heat until beef is no longer pink and onion is tender, 10-12 minutes, breaking meat into crumbles; drain. Stir in squash, parsnips, carrots, cola, tomato paste, water, mustard and seasonings. Cook, covered, on low for 30 to 45 minutes, checking every 15 minutes, until vegetables are tender. Stir in bacon. Serve on buns. Serves 9

Nutritional Information: 1 sandwich: 275 calories, 8g fat, 35mg cholesterol, 35g carbohydrate, 17g protein, 526mg sodium

Banana Peanut Butter Pudding

2 very ripe bananas
1 1/2 cups low fat milk
1/2 cup natural creamy peanut butter
3 tablespoons chia seeds

In a blender, puree the banana, milk and peanut butter. Transfer mixture to a medium bowl and stir in the chia seeds. Cover with plastic wrap and chill in the refrigerator for 4 hours or overnight. Stir before serving. Can be stored in an airtight container refrigerated for up to 1 week. Serves 6

Nutritional Information per serving: 220 calories, 18g carbohydrates, 8g protein, 4mg cholesterol, 127mg sodium

Lasagna Soup

1 pound lean ground beef (90% lean)
1 large green pepper, chopped
1 medium onion, chopped
2 garlic cloves, minced
2 cans (14-1/2 ounces each) diced tomatoes, undrained
2 cans (14-1/2 ounces each) reduced-sodium beef broth
1 can (8 ounces) tomato sauce
1 cup frozen corn
1/4 cup tomato paste
2 teaspoons Italian seasoning
1/4 teaspoon pepper
2-1/2 cups uncooked spiral pasta
1/2 cup shredded Parmesan cheese

In a large saucepan, cook beef, green pepper and onion over medium heat 6-8 minutes or until meat is no longer pink, breaking up beef into crumbles. Add garlic; cook 1 minute longer. Drain. Stir in tomatoes, broth, tomato sauce, corn, tomato paste, Italian seasoning and pepper. Bring to a boil. Stir in pasta. Return to a boil. Reduce heat; simmer, covered, 10-12 minutes or until pasta is tender. Sprinkle with cheese.

Nutritional Information: 1-1/3 cups: 280 calories, 7g fat, 41mg cholesterol, 35g carbohydrate, 20g protein, 572mg sodium

DAY 3 | DINNER

Pepper Jack, Chicken and Peach Quesadillas

1 tsp. honey
½ tsp. lime juice
½ cup reduced-fat sour cream
4 (8-inch) flour tortillas
¾ cup shredded Monterey Jack cheese with jalapeño peppers
1 cup chopped skinless, boneless rotisserie chicken breast
1 cup thinly sliced peeled firm ripe peaches
4 tsp. chopped fresh cilantro
nonstick cooking spray

Combine honey and lime juice in a small bowl, stirring well with a whisk. Stir sour cream into the honey mixture and cover and chill until ready to serve. Place tortillas flat on a work surface. Sprinkle 3 tablespoons of the cheese over half of each tortilla, and then top each tortilla with ¼ cup chicken, ¼ cup peaches and 1 teaspoon cilantro. Fold tortillas in half. Heat a large nonstick skillet over medium-high heat. Coat a pan with nonstick cooking spray, place 2 quesadillas in the pan, and top quesadillas with a cast-iron or other heavy skillet. Cook 1½ minutes on each side or until the tortillas are crisp and lightly browned (leave the cast-iron skillet on the quesadillas as they cook). Remove the quesadillas from pan, set aside and keep warm. Repeat this procedure with the remaining quesadillas. Cut each quesadilla into wedges and serve with sauce. Serves 4.

Nutritional Information: 364 calories, 15.8g fat, 21.3g protein, 33.5g carbohydrate, 68mg cholesterol, 485mg sodium.

Microwave Egg Sandwich

1 piece Canadian bacon
1/4 cup egg substitute
1 tablespoon salsa
1 tablespoon shredded reduced-fat cheddar cheese
1 whole wheat English muffin, split, toasted
3 spinach leaves

Place Canadian bacon on bottom of a 6-oz. ramekin or custard cup coated with cooking spray. Pour egg substitute over top. Microwave, uncovered, on high for 30 seconds; stir. Microwave 15-30 seconds or until egg is almost set. Top with salsa; sprinkle with cheese. Microwave just until cheese is melted, about 10 seconds.

Line bottom of English muffin with spinach. Place egg and Canadian bacon over spinach; replace English muffin top. Serves 1

Nutritional Information: 1 sandwich: 218 calories, 4g fat, 12mg cholesterol, 30g carbohydrate, 17g protein, 751mg sodium

DAY 4 | LUNCH

Spicy Chicken Noodle Soup

1 broiler/fryer chicken (3 to 4 pounds), cut up
2 teaspoons adobo seasoning
2 tablespoons olive oil
2 celery ribs, chopped
1 medium onion, chopped
1 medium carrot, chopped
1/4 cup tomato sauce with garlic
2 quarts water
1 bay leaf
2 medium Yukon Gold potatoes, peeled and cubed
12 ounces uncooked angel hair pasta, broken into 1-inch pieces
1 teaspoon salt
1/2 teaspoon pepper
Fresh cilantro leaves, optional

Sprinkle adobo seasoning over chicken. In a large stockpot, heat oil over medium heat. Brown chicken on both sides in batches. Remove chicken from pot. Add celery, onion, carrot and tomato sauce to same pot; cook and stir until onion is tender, 3-4 minutes. Return chicken to pot. Add water and bay leaf; bring to a boil. Reduce heat; cover and simmer 30 minutes. Add potatoes. Simmer, uncovered, until potatoes are almost tender, 8-10 minutes. Remove chicken and bay leaf; discard bay leaf. Let chicken stand until cool enough to handle. Skim fat from broth. Return broth to a simmer; add noodles. Simmer, uncovered, until noodles are tender, 5-7 minutes.

Meanwhile, remove chicken from bones; discard bones. Cut chicken into bite-sized pieces; add chicken to broth. Add salt and pepper. Cook and stir until heated through. If desired, garnish with cilantro.

Nutritional Information: 1 cup: 324 calories, 12g fat, 52mg cholesterol, 31g carbohydrate, 22g protein, 530mg sodium

Pork & Mushrooms

4 boneless pork loin chops (6 ounces each)
3/4 teaspoon salt, divided
1/8 teaspoon white pepper
3 teaspoons butter, divided
3/4 pound sliced fresh mushrooms
1/2 cup reduced-sodium chicken broth
1/2 teaspoon dried tarragon

Sprinkle pork with 1/2 teaspoon salt and white pepper. In a large nonstick skillet, heat 2 teaspoons butter over medium heat. Add pork chops; cook 5-6 minutes on each side. Remove from pan. In same skillet, heat remaining butter over medium-high heat. Add mushrooms; cook and stir 6-8 minutes or until tender. Add broth, tarragon and remaining salt, stirring to loosen browned bits from pan. Bring to a boil; cook until liquid is reduced by half. Return chops to pan; heat through. Serves 4

Nutritional Information: 1 pork chop with 1/3 cup mushrooms: 299 calories, 13g fat, 89mg cholesterol, 4g carbohydrate, 35g protein, 515mg sodium

DAY 5 | BREAKFAST

Oatmeal Pancakes With Cinnamon Apples

1 1⁄2 cups buttermilk
3⁄4 cup instant rolled oats
3⁄4 cup whole wheat flour
2 Tbsp milk
1 Tbsp melted butter
1 1⁄2 tsp baking powder
1⁄2 tsp baking soda
Pinch of cinnamon (plus 1⁄8 tsp for the apples)
Pinch of nutmeg
1 Granny Smith apple, peeled, cored, and chopped
1⁄2 cup apple juice
2 Tbsp brown sugar
Butter or cooking spray
Confectioners' sugar

In a large mixing bowl, combine the buttermilk, oats, flour, milk, butter, baking powder, baking soda, pinch of cinnamon, and nutmeg. Stir to gently combine, then set aside to rest for a few minutes. Combine the apple, apple juice, brown sugar, and remaining 1⁄8 teaspoon cinnamon in a small saucepan and bring to a simmer. Cook until the apple has softened and the liquid has thickened. Preheat the oven to 200°F. Heat a large nonstick or cast-iron skillet over medium heat. Adding a bit of butter or cooking spray before each round, scoop 1⁄4-cup portions of batter into the skillet and use a spatula to spread into thin, even circles. Cook until small bubbles form in the top of the batter, 2 to 3 minutes, then flip and cook for another 2 minutes. Keep pancakes warm in the oven while you finish cooking. Serve topped with the warm apples and a bit of confectioners' sugar, if you like. Serves 4

Nutritional Information: 248 Calories, 5g Fat, 9g Protein, 43g Carbohydrate, 12mg Cholesterol, 627mg Sodium

Chickpea Salad Sandwich

15 ounce can chickpeas, drained & rinsed
1 rib celery
3 green onions
1 to 2 tablespoons light mayonnaise
1 tablespoon lemon juice
1 teaspoon celery seed
Kosher salt & ground pepper
4 slices whole-grain bread
Lettuce, spring green mix, or sprouts

Thinly slice the celery. Thinly slice the green onions. Drain and rinse the chickpeas. In a medium bowl, smash the chickpeas with a fork. Combine the chickpeas with the chopped celery and green onions, mayonnaise, lemon juice, and celery seed. Season with salt and ground pepper to taste. Can add more mayonnaise if mixture is too dry. Assemble sandwich. Serves 2

Nutritional Information: 384 Calories, 12g Fat, 54g Carbohydrate, 11g Protein, 520mg Sodium

Tortilla Pie

1/2 pound lean ground beef (90% lean)
1/2 cup chopped onion
2 garlic cloves, minced
1 teaspoon chili powder
1/2 teaspoon ground cumin
1 can (14-1/2 ounces) Mexican diced tomatoes, drained
3/4 cup reduced-fat ricotta cheese
1/4 cup shredded part-skim mozzarella cheese
3 tablespoons minced fresh cilantro, divided
4 whole wheat tortillas (8 inches)
1/2 cup shredded cheddar cheese

Preheat oven to 400°. In a large skillet, cook and crumble beef with onion and garlic over medium heat until no longer pink, 4-6 minutes. Stir in spices and tomatoes. Bring to a boil; remove from heat. In a small bowl, mix ricotta cheese, mozzarella cheese and 2 tablespoons cilantro. Place 1 tortilla in a 9-in. round baking pan coated with cooking spray. Layer with half the meat sauce, 1 tortilla, ricotta mixture, another tortilla and remaining meat sauce. Top with remaining tortilla; sprinkle with cheddar cheese and remaining cilantro.
Bake, covered, until heated through, 15-20 minutes. Serves 4

Nutritional Information: 1 serving: 356 calories, 14g fat, 65mg cholesterol, 32g carbohydrate, 25g protein, 574mg sodium

Pear Breakfast Bake

1 cup water
1/4 cup quinoa, rinsed
1/4 cup mashed peeled ripe pear
1 tablespoon honey
1/4 teaspoon ground cinnamon
1/4 teaspoon vanilla extract
Dash ground ginger
Dash ground nutmeg
TOPPING:
1/4 cup sliced almonds
1 tablespoon brown sugar
1 tablespoon butter, softened

Preheat oven to 350°. In a small bowl, combine the first 8 ingredients; transfer to a greased 3-cup baking dish. Cover and bake for 50 minutes. In another small bowl, combine almonds, brown sugar and butter; sprinkle over quinoa mixture. Bake, uncovered, until lightly browned, 5-10 minutes longer. Let stand 10 minutes before serving. If desired, serve with yogurt. Serves 2

Nutritional Information: 1 serving: 267 calories, 13g fat, 15mg cholesterol, 35g carbohydrate, 6g protein, 49mg sodium

Caprese Macaroni Salad

2 cups uncooked elbow macaroni
1 cup mayonnaise
1 tablespoon Italian salad dressing mix
2 teaspoons sugar
3/4 teaspoon ground mustard
1/4 teaspoon salt
1/8 teaspoon pepper
1 pint cherry tomatoes, halved
1 cup fresh mozzarella cheese pearls
1/4 cup fresh basil leaves, slivered
2 tablespoons grated Parmesan cheese

Cook macaroni according to package directions; drain and rinse with cold water. Cool completely. For dressing, in a small bowl, combine mayonnaise, dressing mix, sugar, mustard, salt and pepper. In a large bowl, combine tomatoes, mozzarella and macaroni. Add dressing; gently toss to coat. Refrigerate until serving. Top with basil and Parmesan before serving. Serves 7

Nutritional Information: 3/4 cup: 397 calories, 31g fat, 29mg cholesterol, 20g carbohydrate, 10g protein, 458mg sodium

One-Pan Chicken Curry Dinner

2 pounds sweet potato, peeled and cubed
2 cups fresh cauliflowerets
1 large onion, chopped
3 garlic cloves, minced
2 tablespoons olive oil
2 teaspoons curry powder, divided
1-1/4 teaspoons salt, divided
1 teaspoon lemon-pepper seasoning, divided
6 bone-in chicken thighs (about 2-1/4 pounds), skin removed
1 teaspoon smoked paprika
1/4 cup chicken broth

Preheat oven to 425°. Line an 11x17-in. baking pan with heavy-duty foil. Place sweet potatoes, cauliflower, onion and garlic on prepared pan. Drizzle with oil; sprinkle with 1 teaspoon curry powder, 3/4 teaspoon salt and 1/2 teaspoon lemon pepper; toss to coat. Arrange chicken over vegetables. In a small bowl, mix paprika and remaining 1 teaspoon curry powder, 1/2 teaspoon salt and 1/2 teaspoon lemon-pepper seasoning; sprinkle over chicken. Roast until vegetables are almost tender, 30-35 minutes. Drizzle with broth; bake until thermometer inserted in chicken reads 170°-175° and vegetables are tender, 7-10 minutes longer. Serves 6

Nutritional Information: 409 calories, 14g fat, 87mg cholesterol, 42g carbohydrate, 28g protein, 686mg sodium

Easy Broccoli-Cheese Eggs in a Mug

Nonstick cooking spray
1 cup chopped fresh or frozen broccoli
1 Tbsp chopped red bell pepper
1 green onion (scallion), sliced
2 eggs
2 Tbsp fat-free milk
1/4 cup shredded white cheddar cheese (1 oz)
Salt and black pepper to taste

Generously coat the inside of a 12-ounce mug with cooking spray. Add broccoli and 1 tsp water, and microwave on 100% power (high) for 1 to 2 minutes, or until broccoli is tender. Add red pepper, green onion, eggs, and milk. Beat with a fork until eggs are well blended. Microwave for 45 seconds; stir. Microwave again for 30 seconds, or until eggs are puffed and set. Sprinkle with cheese; cover with foil, and let stand a few minutes until melted. Season with salt and pepper. Serves 1.

Nutritional Information: 300 Calories, 20g Fat, 23g Protein, 8g Carbohydrate, 454mg Cholesterol, 355mg Sodium

Garden Turkey Sandwich with Lemon Mayo

1 cup cherry or tomatoes, quartered

1 tsp. grated lemon peel

1 tbsp. low-fat mayonnaise

2 slices whole-grain bread

1 cup loosely packed baby spinach leaves

2 oz. turkey breast, sliced

1 small tomato, sliced

Stir the grated lemon peel into the mayonnaise and spread on both slices of bread. On one slice of the bread, alternately layer spinach leaves, turkey and tomato, starting and ending with spinach. Top with the second bread slice. Serves 1.

Nutritional Information: 300 calories, 7g fat, 57mg cholesterol, 33g carbohydrate, 26g protein, 320mg sodium

DAY 7 | DINNER

Pan-Fried Chicken Fingers with Spicy Dipping Sauce

¼ cup canola mayonnaise
2 tsp. hot chili sauce
1 tsp. fresh lime juice
½ tsp. low-sodium soy sauce
¼ cup all-purpose flour
1½ tsp. freshly ground black pepper
1½ tsp. paprika
2 large eggs, lightly beaten
1 tbsp. water
3 cups whole-grain flake cereal
1 lb. chicken breast tenders
¼ tsp. salt
1½ tbsp. canola oil

To prepare sauce, combine the mayonnaise, chili sauce, lime juice and soy sauce in a small bowl, stirring with a whisk. Cover and chill. To prepare the chicken, combine the flour, black pepper and paprika and place the mixture in a shallow dish. Combine eggs and 1 tablespoon water, and place in another shallow dish. Place the crushed cereal in another shallow dish. Sprinkle the chicken evenly with salt and then, working with 1 piece at a time, dredge the chicken in the flour mixture. Dip the chicken in the egg mixture, and then dredge in the cereal. Next, heat a large skillet over medium-high heat. Add oil to the pan, swirling to coat. Add chicken pieces to pan, and cook for 2 minutes on each side or until done. Serve immediately with sauce. Serves 4.

Nutritional Information: 414 calories, 14g fat, 156mg cholesterol, 495mg, 38g carbohydrate, 540mg sodium.

STEPS FOR SPIRITUAL GROWTH

—— GOD'S WORD FOR YOUR LIFE

I have hidden your word in my heart that I might not sin against you.

Psalm 119:11

As you begin to make decisions based on what God's Word teaches you, you will want to memorize what He has promised to those who trust and follow Him. Second Peter 1:3 tells us that God "has given us everything we need for life and godliness through our knowledge of him" (emphasis added). The Bible provides instruction and encouragement for any area of life in which you may be struggling. If you are dealing with a particular emotion or traumatic life event—fear, discouragement, stress, financial upset, the death of a loved one, a relationship difficulty—you can search through a Bible concordance for Scripture passages that deal with that particular situation. Scripture provides great comfort to those who memorize it.

One of the promises of knowing and obeying God's Word is that it gives you wisdom, insight, and understanding above all worldly knowledge (see Psalm 119:97–104). Psalm 119:129–130 says, "Your statutes are wonderful; therefore I obey them. The unfolding of your words gives light; it gives understanding to the simple." Now that's a precious promise about guidance for life!

The Value of Scripture Memory

Scripture memory is an important part of the Christian life. There are four key reasons to memorize Scripture:

11. **TO HANDLE DIFFICULT SITUATIONS.** A heartfelt knowledge of God's Word will equip you to handle any situation that you might face. Declaring such truth as, "I can do everything through Christ" (see Philippians 4:13) and "he will never leave me or forsake me" (see Hebrews 13:5) will enable you to walk through situations with peace and courage.

12. **TO OVERCOME TEMPTATION.** Luke 4:1–13 describes how Jesus used Scripture to overcome His temptations in the desert (see also Matthew 4:1–11). Knowledge of Scripture and the strength that comes with the ability to use it are important parts of putting on the full armor of God in preparation for spiritual warfare (see Ephesians 6:10–18).

13. **TO GET GUIDANCE.** Psalm 119:105 states the Word of God "is a lamp to my feet and a light for my path." You learn to hide God's Word in your heart so His light will direct your decisions and actions throughout your day.

14. **TO TRANSFORM YOUR MIND.** "Do not conform any longer to the pattern of this world, but be transformed by the renewing of your mind" (Romans 12:2). Scripture memory allows you to replace a lie with the truth of God's Word. When Scripture becomes firmly settled in your memory, not only will your thoughts connect with God's thoughts, but you will also be able to honor God with small everyday decisions as well as big life-impacting ones. Scripture memorization is the key to making a permanent lifestyle change in your thought patterns, which brings balance to every other area of your life.

Scripture Memory Tips

- Write the verse down, saying it aloud as you write it.
- Read verses before and after the memory verse to get its context.
- Read the verse several times, emphasizing a different word each time.
- Connect the Scripture reference to the first few words.
- Locate patterns, phrases, or keywords.
- Apply the Scripture to circumstances you are now experiencing.
- Pray the verse, making it personal to your life and inserting your name as the recipient of the promise or teaching. (Try that with 1 Corinthians 10:13, inserting "me" and "I" for "you.")
- Review the verse every day until it becomes second nature to think those words whenever your circumstances match its message. The Holy Spirit will bring the verse to mind when you need it most if you decide to plant it in your memory.

Scripture Memorization Made Easy!

What is your learning style? Do you learn by hearing, by sight, or by doing?

If you learn by hearing—if you are an auditory learner—singing the Scripture memory verses, reading them aloud, or recording them and listening to your recording will be very helpful in the memorization process.

If you are a visual learner, writing the verses and repeatedly reading through them will cement them in your mind.

If you learn by doing—if you are a tactile learner—creating motions for the words or using sign language will enable you to more easily recall the verse.

After determining your learning style, link your Scripture memory with a daily task, such as driving to work, walking on a treadmill, or eating lunch. Use these daily tasks as opportunities to memorize and review your verses.

Meals at home or out with friends can be used as a time to share the verse you are memorizing with those at your table. You could close your personal email messages by typing in your weekly memory verse. Or why not say your memory verse every time you brush your teeth or put on your shoes?

The purpose of Scripture memorization is to be able to apply God's words to your life. If you memorize Scripture using methods that connect with your particular learning style, you will find it easier to hide God's Word in your heart.

—— ESTABLISHING A QUIET TIME

Like all other components of the First Place for Health program, developing a live relationship with God is not a random act. You must intentionally seek God if you are to find Him! It's not that God plays hide-and-seek with you. He is always available to you. He invites you to come boldly into His presence. He reveals Himself to you in the pages of the Bible. And once you decide to earnestly seek Him, you are sure to find Him! When you delight in Him, your gracious God will give you the desires of your heart. Spending time getting to know God involves four basic elements: a priority, a plan, a place, and practice.

A Priority

You can successfully establish a quiet time with God by making this meeting a daily priority. This may require carving out time in your day so you have time and space for this new relationship you are cultivating. Often this will mean eliminating less important things so you will have time and space to meet with God. When speaking about Jesus, John the Baptist said, "He must become greater; I must become less" (John 3:30). You will undoubtedly find that to be true as well. What might you need to eliminate from your current schedule so that spending quality time with God can become a priority?

A Plan

Having made quiet time a priority, you will want to come up with a plan. This plan will include the time you have set aside to spend with God and a general outline of how you will spend your time in God's presence.

Elements you should consider incorporating into your quiet time include:

- Singing a song of praise
- Reading a daily selection in a devotional book or reading a psalm
- Using a systematic Scripture reading plan so you will be exposed to the whole truth of God's Word
- Completing your First Place for Health Bible study for that day
- Praying—silent, spoken, and written prayer
- Writing in your spiritual journal.

You will also want to make a list of the materials you will need to make your encounter with God more meaningful:

- A Bible
- Your First Place for Health Bible study
- Your prayer journal
- A pen and/or pencil
- A devotional book
- A Bible concordance
- A college-level dictionary
- A box of tissues (tears—both of sadness and joy—are often part of our quiet time with God!)

Think of how you would plan an important business meeting or social event, and then transfer that knowledge to your meeting time with God.

A Place

Having formulated a meeting-with-God plan, you will next need to create a meeting-with-God place. Of course, God is always with you; however, in order to have quality devotional time with Him, it is desirable that you find a comfortable meeting place. You will want to select a spot that is quiet and as distraction-free as possible. Meeting with God in the same place on a regular basis will help you remember what you are there for: to have an encounter with the true and living God!

Having selected the place, put the materials you have determined to use in your quiet time into a basket or on a nearby table or shelf. Now take the time to establish your personal quiet time with God. Tailor your quiet time to fit your needs—and the time you have allotted to spend with God. Although many people elect to meet with God early in the morning, for others afternoon or evening is best. There is no hard-and-fast rule about when your quiet time should be—the only essential thing is that you establish a quiet time!

Start with a small amount of time that you know you can devote yourself to daily. You can be confident that as you consistently spend time with God each day, the amount of time you can spend will increase as you are ready for the next level of your walk with God.

I will meet with God from _____ to _____ daily.

I plan to use that time with God to _____

_____

Supplies I will need to assemble include _____

_____

My meeting place with God will be _____

_____

Practice

After you have chosen the time and place to meet God each day and you have assembled your supplies, there are four easy steps for having a fruitful and worshipful time with the Lord.

STEP 1: Clear Your Heart and Mind

"Be still, and know that I am God" (Psalm 46:10). Begin your quiet time by reading the daily Bible selection from a devotional guide or a psalm. If you are new in your Christian walk, an excellent devotional guide to use is *Streams in the Desert* by L.B. Cowman. More mature Christians might benefit from *My Utmost for His Highest* by Oswald Chambers. Of course, you can use any devotional that has a strong emphasis on Scripture and prayer.

STEP 2: Read and Interact with Scripture

"I have hidden your word in my heart that I might not sin against you" (Psalm 119:11). As you open your Bible, ask the Holy Spirit to reveal something He knows you need for this day through the reading of His Word. Always try to find a nugget to encourage or direct you through the day. As you read the passage, pay special attention to the words and phrases the Holy Spirit brings to your attention. Some words may seem to resonate in your soul. You will want to spend time meditating on the passage, asking God what lesson He is teaching you.

After reading the Scripture passage over several times, ask yourself the following questions:

- In light of what I have read today, is there something I must now do? (Confess a sin? Claim a promise? Follow an example? Obey a command? Avoid a situation?)
- How should I respond to what I've read today?

STEP 3: Pray

"Be clear minded and self-controlled so that you can pray" (1 Peter 4:7). Spend time conversing with the Lord in prayer. Prayer is such an important part of First Place for Health that there is an entire section in this member's guide devoted to the practice of prayer.

STEP 4: Praise

"Praise the LORD, O my soul, and forget not all his benefits" (Psalm 103:2). End your quiet time with a time of praise. Be sure to thank the Lord of heaven and warmth for choosing to spend time with you!

—— SHARING YOUR FAITH

Nothing is more effective in drawing someone to Jesus than sharing personal life experiences. People are more open to the good news of Jesus Christ when they see faith in action. Personal faith stories are simple and effective ways to share what Christ is doing in your life, because they show firsthand how Christ makes a difference.

Sharing your faith story has an added benefit: it builds you up in your faith, too! Is your experience in First Place for Health providing you opportunities to share with others what God is doing in your life? If you answered yes, then you have a personal faith story!

If you do not have a personal faith story, perhaps it is because you don't know Jesus Christ as your personal Lord and Savior. Read through "Steps to Becoming a Christian" (which is the next chapter) and begin today to give Christ first place in your life.

Creativity and preparation in using opportunities to share a word or story about Jesus is an important part of the Christian life. Is Jesus helping you in a special way? Are you achieving a level of success or peace that you haven't experienced in other attempts to lose weight, exercise regularly, or eat healthier? As people see you making changes and achieving success, they may ask you how you are doing it. How will—or do—you respond? Remember, your story is unique, and it may allow others to see what Christ is doing in your life. It may also help to bring Christ into the life of another person.

Personal Statements of Faith

First Place for Health gives you a great opportunity to communicate your faith and express what God is doing in your life. Be ready to use your own personal statement of faith whenever the opportunity presents itself. Personal statements of faith should be short and fit naturally into a conversation. They don't require or expect any action or response from the listener. The goal is not to get another person to change but simply to help you communicate who you are and what's important to you.

Here are some examples of short statements of faith that you might use when someone asks what you are doing to lose weight:

- "I've been meeting with a group at my church. We pray together, support each other, learn about nutrition, and study the Bible."
- "It's amazing how Bible study and prayer are helping me lose weight and eat healthier."
- "I've had a lot of support from a group I meet with at church."
- "I'm relying more on God to help me make changes in my lifestyle."

Begin keeping a list of your meaningful experiences as you go through the First Place for Health program. Also notice what is happening in the lives of others. Use the following questions to help you prepare short personal statements and stories of faith:

- What is God doing in your life physically, mentally, emotionally, and spiritually?
- How has your relationship with God changed? Is it more intimate or personal?
- How is prayer, Bible study, and/or the support of others helping you achieve your goals for a healthy weight and good nutrition?

Writing Your Personal Faith Story

Write a brief story about how God is working in your life through First Place for Health. Use your story to help you share with others what's happening in your life.

Use the following questions to help develop your story:

- Why did you join First Place for Health? What specific circumstances led you to a Christ-centered health and weight-loss program? What were you feeling when you joined?
- What was your relationship with Christ when you started First Place for Health? What is it now?
- Has your experience in First Place for Health changed your relationship with Christ? With yourself? With others?
- How has your relationship with Christ, prayer, Bible study, and group support made a difference in your life?
- What specific verse or passage of Scripture has made a difference in the way you view yourself or your relationship with Christ?
- What experiences have impacted your life since starting First Place for Health?
- In what ways is Christ working in your life today? In what ways is He meeting your needs?
- How has Christ worked in other members of your First Place for Health group?

Answer the above questions in a few sentences, and then use your answers to help you write your own short personal faith story.

MEMBER SURVEY

We would love to know more about you. Share this form with your leader.

Name _____ Birth date _____

Tell us about your family.

_____

_____

_____

_____

Would you like to receive more information   Yes   No
about our church?

What area of expertise would you be willing to share with our class?

_____

_____

Why did you join First Place for Health?

_____

_____

With notice, would you be willing to lead a Bible study   Yes   No
discussion one week?

Are you comfortable praying out loud?   _____

Would you be willing to assist recording weights and/or   Yes   No
evaluating the Live It Trackers?

Any other comments:

_____

_____

PERSONAL WEIGHT AND MEASUREMENT RECORD

WEEK	WEIGHT	+ OR -	GOAL THIS SESSION	POUNDS TO GOAL
1				
2				
3				
4				
5				
6				
7				
8				
9				
10				
11				
12				

BEGINNING MEASUREMENTS

WAIST_____ HIPS_____ THIGHS_____ CHEST_____

ENDING MEASUREMENTS

WAIST_____ HIPS_____ THIGHS_____ CHEST_____

If you cling to your life, you will lose it; but if you give up your life for me,
you will find it. Matthew 10:39 NLT

Date: _____

Name: _____

Home Phone: _____

Cell Phone: _____

Email: _____

Personal Prayer Concerns

_____

_____

_____

_____

_____

_____

_____

This form is for prayer requests that are personal to you and your journey in First Place for Health.
Please complete and have it ready to turn in when you arrive at your group meeting.

*Blessed are the meek, for they will inherit
the earth. Matthew 5:5*

Date: _____

Name: _____

Home Phone: _____

Cell Phone: _____

Email: _____

Personal Prayer Concerns

_____

_____

_____

_____

_____

_____

_____

_____

This form is for prayer requests that are personal to you and your journey in First Place for Health.
Please complete and have it ready to turn in when you arrive at your group meeting.

Jesus said to him, "If you wish to be complete, go and sell your possessions and give to the poor, and you will have treasure in heaven, and come, follow Me." Matthew 19:21 LSB

Date: _____

Name: _____

Home Phone: _____

Cell Phone: _____

Email: _____

Personal Prayer Concerns

_____

_____

_____

_____

_____

_____

_____

This form is for prayer requests that are personal to you and your journey in First Place for Health. Please complete and have it ready to turn in when you arrive at your group meeting.

Blessed are those who hunger and thirst for righteousness, for they will be filled. Matthew 5:6

Date: _____

Name: _____

Home Phone: _____

Cell Phone: _____

Email: _____

Personal Prayer Concerns

_____

_____

_____

_____

_____

_____

_____

_____

This form is for prayer requests that are personal to you and your journey in First Place for Health. Please complete and have it ready to turn in when you arrive at your group meeting.

Whoever wants to become great among you must be your servant, and whoever wants to be first must be your slave— just as the Son of Man did not come to be served, but to serve, and to give his life as a ransom for many. Matthew 20:26-28

Date: _____

Name: _____

Home Phone: _____

Cell Phone: _____

Email: _____

Personal Prayer Concerns

_____

_____

_____

_____

_____

_____

_____

This form is for prayer requests that are personal to you and your journey in First Place for Health. Please complete and have it ready to turn in when you arrive at your group meeting.

For we live by faith, not by sight. 2 Corinthians 5:7

Date: _____

Name: _____

Home Phone: _____

Cell Phone: _____

Email: _____

Personal Prayer Concerns

_____

_____

_____

_____

_____

_____

_____

_____

This form is for prayer requests that are personal to you and your journey in First Place for Health. Please complete and have it ready to turn in when you arrive at your group meeting.

Consider it all joy, my brothers and sisters, when you encounter various trials,
knowing that the testing of your faith produces endurance. And let endurance have its
perfect result, so that you may be perfect and complete, lacking in nothing. James 1:2-4 NASB

Date: _____

Name: _____

Home Phone: _____

Cell Phone: _____

Email: _____

Personal Prayer Concerns

_____

_____

_____

_____

_____

_____

_____

This form is for prayer requests that are personal to you and your journey in First Place for Health. Please complete and have it ready to turn in when you arrive at your group meeting.

*Therefore, everyone who hears these words of mine and puts them into
practice is like a wise man who built his house on the rock. The rain came down, the streams rose,
and the winds blew and beat against that house; yet it did not fall, because it had its foundation
on the rock. Matthew 7:24-25*

Date: _____

Name: _____

Home Phone: _____

Cell Phone: _____

Email: _____

Personal Prayer Concern

_____

_____

_____

_____

_____

_____

_____

This form is for prayer requests that are personal to you and your journey in First Place for Health.
Please complete and have it ready to turn in when you arrive at your group meeting.

PRAYER PARTNER

Date: _____

Name: _____

Home Phone: _____

Cell Phone: _____

Email: _____

Personal Prayer Concerns

_____

_____

_____

_____

_____

_____

_____

_____

This form is for prayer requests that are personal to you and your journey in First Place for Health. Please complete and have it ready to turn in when you arrive at your group meeting.

LIVE IT TRACKER

Name: _____ Date: _____ Week #: _____

My activity goal for next week:

○ None   ○ <30 min/day   ○ 30-60 min/day

My food goal for next week: _____

_____

loss/gain _____ Calorie Range: _____

My week at a glance:

○ Great   ○ So-so   ○ Not so great

Activity level:

○ None   ○ <30 min/day   ○ 30-60 min/day

RECOMMENDED DAILY AMOUNT OF FOOD FROM EACH GROUP

GROUP	DAILY CALORIES							
	1300-1400	1500-1600	1700-1800	1900-2000	2100-2200	2300-2400	2500-2600	2700-2800
Fruits	1.5 – 2 c.	1.5 – 2 c.	1.5 – 2 c.	2 – 2.5 c.	2 – 2.5 c.	2.5 – 3.5 c.	3.5 – 4.5 c.	3.5 – 4.5 c.
Vegetables	1.5 – 2 c.	2 – 2.5 c.	2.5 – 3 c.	2.5 – 3 c.	3 – 3.5 c.	3.5 – 4.5 c..	4.5 – 5 c.	4.5 – 5 c.
Grains	5 oz eq.	5-6 oz eq.	6-7 oz eq.	6-7 oz eq.	7-8 oz eq.	8-9 oz eq.	9-10 oz eq.	10-11 oz eq.
Dairy	2-3 c.	3 c.	3 c.	3 c.	3 c.	3 c.	3 c.	3 c.
Protein	4 oz eq.	5 oz eq.	5-5.5 oz eq.	5.5-6.5 oz eq.	6.5-7 oz eq.	7-7.5 oz eq.	7-7.5 oz eq.	7.5-8 oz eq.
Healthy Oils & Other Fats	4 tsp.	5 tsp.	5 tsp.	6 tsp.	6 tsp.	7 tsp.	8 tsp.	8 tsp.
Water & Super Beverages*	Women: 9 c. Men: 13 c.	Women: 9 c. Men: 13 c.	Women: 9 c. Men: 13 c.	Women: 9 c. Men: 13 c.	Women: 9 c. Men: 13 c.	Women: 9 c. Men: 13 c.	Women: 9 c. Men: 13 c.	Women: 9 c. Men: 13 c.

*May count up to 3 cups caffeinated tea or coffee toward goal

DAILY FOOD GROUP TRACKER

GROUP	FRUITS	VEGETABLES	GRAINS	PROTEIN	DAIRY	HEALTHY OILS & OTHER FATS	WATER & SUPER BEVERAGES
1 Estimate Total							
2 Estimate Total							
3 Estimate Total							
4 Estimate Total							
5 Estimate Total							
6 Estimate Total							
7 Estimate Total							

FOOD CHOICES   DAY ❶

Breakfast: _____

Lunch: _____

Dinner: _____

Snacks: _____

PHYSICAL ACTIVITY   steps/miles/minutes: _____

description: _____

SPIRITUAL ACTIVITY

description: _____

FOOD CHOICES

DAY ❷

Breakfast: _____

Lunch: _____

Dinner: _____

Snacks: _____

PHYSICAL ACTIVITY   steps/miles/minutes: _____

description: _____

SPIRITUAL ACTIVITY

description: _____

FOOD CHOICES

DAY ❸

Breakfast: _____

Lunch: _____

Dinner: _____

Snacks: _____

PHYSICAL ACTIVITY   steps/miles/minutes: _____

description: _____

SPIRITUAL ACTIVITY

description: _____

FOOD CHOICES

DAY ❹

Breakfast: _____

Lunch: _____

Dinner: _____

Snacks: _____

PHYSICAL ACTIVITY   steps/miles/minutes: _____

description: _____

SPIRITUAL ACTIVITY

description: _____

FOOD CHOICES

DAY ❺

Breakfast: _____

Lunch: _____

Dinner: _____

Snacks: _____

PHYSICAL ACTIVITY   steps/miles/minutes: _____

description: _____

SPIRITUAL ACTIVITY

description: _____

FOOD CHOICES

DAY ❻

Breakfast: _____

Lunch: _____

Dinner: _____

Snacks: _____

PHYSICAL ACTIVITY   steps/miles/minutes: _____

description: _____

SPIRITUAL ACTIVITY

description: _____

FOOD CHOICES

DAY ❼

Breakfast: _____

Lunch: _____

Dinner: _____

Snacks: _____

PHYSICAL ACTIVITY   steps/miles/minutes: _____

description: _____

SPIRITUAL ACTIVITY

description: _____

LIVE IT TRACKER

Name: _____   Date: _____ Week #: _____

My activity goal for next week:
○ None   ○ <30 min/day   ○ 30-60 min/day

loss/gain _____   Calorie Range: _____

My food goal for next week: _____

My week at a glance:
○ Great   ○ So-so   ○ Not so great

Activity level:
○ None   ○ <30 min/day   ○ 30-60 min/day

RECOMMENDED DAILY AMOUNT OF FOOD FROM EACH GROUP

GROUP	DAILY CALORIES							
	1300-1400	1500-1600	1700-1800	1900-2000	2100-2200	2300-2400	2500-2600	2700-2800
Fruits	1.5 – 2 c.	1.5 – 2 c.	1.5 – 2 c.	2 – 2.5 c.	2 – 2.5 c.	2.5 – 3.5 c.	3.5 – 4.5 c.	3.5 – 4.5 c.
Vegetables	1.5 – 2 c.	2 – 2.5 c.	2.5 – 3 c.	2.5 – 3 c.	3 – 3.5 c.	3.5 – 4.5 c.	4.5 – 5 c.	4.5 – 5 c.
Grains	5 oz eq.	5-6 oz eq.	6-7 oz eq.	6-7 oz eq.	7-8 oz eq.	8-9 oz eq.	9-10 oz eq.	10-11 oz eq.
Dairy	2-3 c.	3 c.	3 c.	3 c.	3 c.	3 c.	3 c.	3 c.
Protein	4 oz eq.	5 oz eq.	5-5.5 oz eq.	5.5-6.5 oz eq.	6.5-7 oz eq.	7-7.5 oz eq.	7-7.5 oz eq.	7.5-8 oz eq.
Healthy Oils & Other Fats	4 tsp.	5 tsp.	5 tsp.	6 tsp.	6 tsp.	7 tsp.	8 tsp.	8 tsp.
Water & Super Beverages*	Women: 9 c. Men: 13 c.	Women: 9 c. Men: 13 c.	Women: 9 c. Men: 13 c.	Women: 9 c. Men: 13 c.	Women: 9 c. Men: 13 c.	Women: 9 c. Men: 13 c.	Women: 9 c. Men: 13 c.	Women: 9 c. Men: 13 c.

*May count up to 3 cups caffeinated tea or coffee toward goal

DAILY FOOD GROUP TRACKER

GROUP	FRUITS	VEGETABLES	GRAINS	PROTEIN	DAIRY	HEALTHY OILS & OTHER FATS	WATER & SUPER BEVERAGES
1 Estimate Total							
2 Estimate Total							
3 Estimate Total							
4 Estimate Total							
5 Estimate Total							
6 Estimate Total							
7 Estimate Total							

FOOD CHOICES   DAY ❶

Breakfast: _____
Lunch: _____
Dinner: _____
Snacks: _____

PHYSICAL ACTIVITY   steps/miles/minutes: _____

description: _____

SPIRITUAL ACTIVITY

description: _____

FOOD CHOICES
DAY ❷

Breakfast: _____
Lunch: _____
Dinner: _____
Snacks: _____

PHYSICAL ACTIVITY	steps/miles/minutes: _____	SPIRITUAL ACTIVITY
description: _____		description: _____

FOOD CHOICES
DAY ❸

Breakfast: _____
Lunch: _____
Dinner: _____
Snacks: _____

PHYSICAL ACTIVITY	steps/miles/minutes: _____	SPIRITUAL ACTIVITY
description: _____		description: _____

FOOD CHOICES
DAY ❹

Breakfast: _____
Lunch: _____
Dinner: _____
Snacks: _____

PHYSICAL ACTIVITY	steps/miles/minutes: _____	SPIRITUAL ACTIVITY
description: _____		description: _____

FOOD CHOICES
DAY ❺

Breakfast: _____
Lunch: _____
Dinner: _____
Snacks: _____

PHYSICAL ACTIVITY	steps/miles/minutes: _____	SPIRITUAL ACTIVITY
description: _____		description: _____

FOOD CHOICES
DAY ❻

Breakfast: _____
Lunch: _____
Dinner: _____
Snacks: _____

PHYSICAL ACTIVITY	steps/miles/minutes: _____	SPIRITUAL ACTIVITY
description: _____		description: _____

FOOD CHOICES
DAY ❼

Breakfast: _____
Lunch: _____
Dinner: _____
Snacks: _____

PHYSICAL ACTIVITY	steps/miles/minutes: _____	SPIRITUAL ACTIVITY
description: _____		description: _____

LIVE IT TRACKER

Name: _____   Date: _____ Week #: _____

My activity goal for next week:
○ None   ○ <30 min/day   ○ 30-60 min/day

My food goal for next week: _____

loss/gain _____ Calorie Range: _____

My week at a glance:
○ Great   ○ So-so   ○ Not so great

Activity level:
○ None   ○ <30 min/day   ○ 30-60 min/day

RECOMMENDED DAILY AMOUNT OF FOOD FROM EACH GROUP

GROUP	DAILY CALORIES							
	1300-1400	1500-1600	1700-1800	1900-2000	2100-2200	2300-2400	2500-2600	2700-2800
Fruits	1.5 – 2 c.	1.5 – 2 c.	1.5 – 2 c.	2 – 2.5 c.	2 – 2.5 c.	2.5 – 3.5 c.	3.5 – 4.5 c.	3.5 – 4.5 c.
Vegetables	1.5 – 2 c.	2 – 2.5 c.	2.5 – 3 c.	2.5 – 3 c.	3 – 3.5 c.	3.5 – 4.5 c..	4.5 – 5 c.	4.5 – 5 c.
Grains	5 oz eq.	5-6 oz eq.	6-7 oz eq.	6-7 oz eq.	7-8 oz eq.	8-9 oz eq.	9-10 oz eq.	10-11 oz eq.
Dairy	2-3 c.	3 c.	3 c.	3 c.	3 c.	3 c.	3 c.	3 c.
Protein	4 oz eq.	5 oz eq.	5-5.5 oz eq.	5.5-6.5 oz eq.	6.5-7 oz eq.	7-7.5 oz eq.	7-7.5 oz eq.	7.5-8 oz eq.
Healthy Oils & Other Fats	4 tsp.	5 tsp.	5 tsp.	6 tsp.	6 tsp.	7 tsp.	8 tsp.	8 tsp.
Water & Super Beverages*	Women: 9 c. Men: 13 c.	Women: 9 c. Men: 13 c.	Women: 9 c. Men: 13 c.	Women: 9 c. Men: 13 c.	Women: 9 c. Men: 13 c.	Women: 9 c. Men: 13 c.	Women: 9 c. Men: 13 c.	Women: 9 c. Men: 13 c.

*May count up to 3 cups caffeinated tea or coffee toward goal

DAILY FOOD GROUP TRACKER

GROUP	FRUITS	VEGETABLES	GRAINS	PROTEIN	DAIRY	HEALTHY OILS & OTHER FATS	WATER & SUPER BEVERAGES
1 Estimate Total							
2 Estimate Total							
3 Estimate Total							
4 Estimate Total							
5 Estimate Total							
6 Estimate Total							
7 Estimate Total							

FOOD CHOICES   DAY ❶

Breakfast: _____
Lunch: _____
Dinner: _____
Snacks: _____

PHYSICAL ACTIVITY   steps/miles/minutes: _____   ## SPIRITUAL ACTIVITY

description: _____   description: _____

FOOD CHOICES

DAY ❷

Breakfast: _____

Lunch: _____

Dinner: _____

Snacks: _____

PHYSICAL ACTIVITY   steps/miles/minutes: _____   SPIRITUAL ACTIVITY

description: _____   description: _____

FOOD CHOICES

DAY ❸

Breakfast: _____

Lunch: _____

Dinner: _____

Snacks: _____

PHYSICAL ACTIVITY   steps/miles/minutes: _____   SPIRITUAL ACTIVITY

description: _____   description: _____

FOOD CHOICES

DAY ❹

Breakfast: _____

Lunch: _____

Dinner: _____

Snacks: _____

PHYSICAL ACTIVITY   steps/miles/minutes: _____   SPIRITUAL ACTIVITY

description: _____   description: _____

FOOD CHOICES

DAY ❺

Breakfast: _____

Lunch: _____

Dinner: _____

Snacks: _____

PHYSICAL ACTIVITY   steps/miles/minutes: _____   SPIRITUAL ACTIVITY

description: _____   description: _____

FOOD CHOICES

DAY ❻

Breakfast: _____

Lunch: _____

Dinner: _____

Snacks: _____

PHYSICAL ACTIVITY   steps/miles/minutes: _____   SPIRITUAL ACTIVITY

description: _____   description: _____

FOOD CHOICES

DAY ❼

Breakfast: _____

Lunch: _____

Dinner: _____

Snacks: _____

PHYSICAL ACTIVITY   steps/miles/minutes: _____   SPIRITUAL ACTIVITY

description: _____   description: _____

LIVE IT TRACKER

Name: _____

Date: _____ Week #: _____

My activity goal for next week:
○ None ○ <30 min/day ○ 30-60 min/day

loss /gain _____ Calorie Range: _____

My week at a glance:
○ Great ○ So-so ○ Not so great

My food goal for next week: _____

Activity level:
○ None ○ <30 min/day ○ 30-60 min/day

RECOMMENDED DAILY AMOUNT OF FOOD FROM EACH GROUP

GROUP	DAILY CALORIES							
	1300-1400	1500-1600	1700-1800	1900-2000	2100-2200	2300-2400	2500-2600	2700-2800
Fruits	1.5 – 2 c.	1.5 – 2 c.	1.5 – 2 c.	2 – 2.5 c.	2 – 2.5 c.	2.5 – 3.5 c.	3.5 – 4.5 c.	3.5 – 4.5 c.
Vegetables	1.5 – 2 c.	2 – 2.5 c.	2.5 – 3 c.	2.5 – 3 c.	3 – 3.5 c.	3.5 – 4.5 c..	4.5 – 5 c.	4.5 – 5 c.
Grains	5 oz eq.	5-6 oz eq.	6-7 oz eq.	6-7 oz eq.	7-8 oz eq.	8-9 oz eq.	9-10 oz eq.	10-11 oz eq.
Dairy	2-3 c.	3 c.	3 c.	3 c.	3 c.	3 c.	3 c.	3 c.
Protein	4 oz eq.	5 oz eq.	5-5.5 oz eq.	5.5-6.5 oz eq.	6.5-7 oz eq.	7-7.5 oz eq.	7-7.5 oz eq.	7.5-8 oz eq.
Healthy Oils & Other Fats	4 tsp.	5 tsp.	5 tsp.	6 tsp.	6 tsp.	7 tsp.	8 tsp.	8 tsp.
Water & Super Beverages*	Women: 9 c. Men: 13 c.	Women: 9 c. Men: 13 c.	Women: 9 c. Men: 13 c.	Women: 9 c. Men: 13 c.	Women: 9 c. Men: 13 c.	Women: 9 c. Men: 13 c.	Women: 9 c. Men: 13 c.	Women: 9 c. Men: 13 c.

*May count up to 3 cups caffeinated tea or coffee toward goal

DAILY FOOD GROUP TRACKER

GROUP	FRUITS	VEGETABLES	GRAINS	PROTEIN	DAIRY	HEALTHY OILS & OTHER FATS	WATER & SUPER BEVERAGES
1 Estimate Total							
2 Estimate Total							
3 Estimate Total							
4 Estimate Total							
5 Estimate Total							
6 Estimate Total							
7 Estimate Total							

FOOD CHOICES

DAY ❶

Breakfast: _____
Lunch: _____
Dinner: _____
Snacks: _____

PHYSICAL ACTIVITY   steps/miles/minutes: _____

SPIRITUAL ACTIVITY

description: _____

description: _____

FOOD CHOICES   DAY ❷

Breakfast: _____
Lunch: _____
Dinner: _____
Snacks: _____

PHYSICAL ACTIVITY steps/miles/minutes: _____	SPIRITUAL ACTIVITY
description: _____	description: _____
_____	_____

FOOD CHOICES   DAY ❸

Breakfast: _____
Lunch: _____
Dinner: _____
Snacks: _____

PHYSICAL ACTIVITY steps/miles/minutes: _____	SPIRITUAL ACTIVITY
description: _____	description: _____
_____	_____

FOOD CHOICES   DAY ❹

Breakfast: _____
Lunch: _____
Dinner: _____
Snacks: _____

PHYSICAL ACTIVITY steps/miles/minutes: _____	SPIRITUAL ACTIVITY
description: _____	description: _____
_____	_____

FOOD CHOICES   DAY ❺

Breakfast: _____
Lunch: _____
Dinner: _____
Snacks: _____

PHYSICAL ACTIVITY steps/miles/minutes: _____	SPIRITUAL ACTIVITY
description: _____	description: _____
_____	_____

FOOD CHOICES   DAY ❻

Breakfast: _____
Lunch: _____
Dinner: _____
Snacks: _____

PHYSICAL ACTIVITY steps/miles/minutes: _____	SPIRITUAL ACTIVITY
description: _____	description: _____
_____	_____

FOOD CHOICES   DAY ❼

Breakfast: _____
Lunch: _____
Dinner: _____
Snacks: _____

PHYSICAL ACTIVITY steps/miles/minutes: _____	SPIRITUAL ACTIVITY
description: _____	description: _____
_____	_____

LIVE IT TRACKER

Name: _____   Date: _____ Week #: _____

My activity goal for next week:
○ None   ○ <30 min/day   ○ 30-60 min/day

loss / gain _____   Calorie Range: _____

My week at a glance:
○ Great   ○ So-so   ○ Not so great

My food goal for next week: _____

Activity level:
○ None   ○ <30 min/day   ○ 30-60 min/day

RECOMMENDED DAILY AMOUNT OF FOOD FROM EACH GROUP

GROUP	DAILY CALORIES							
	1300-1400	1500-1600	1700-1800	1900-2000	2100-2200	2300-2400	2500-2600	2700-2800
Fruits	1.5 – 2 c.	1.5 – 2 c.	1.5 – 2 c.	2 – 2.5 c.	2 – 2.5 c.	2.5 – 3.5 c.	3.5 – 4.5 c.	3.5 – 4.5 c.
Vegetables	1.5 – 2 c.	2 – 2.5 c.	2.5 – 3 c.	2.5 – 3 c.	3 – 3.5 c.	3.5 – 4.5 c..	4.5 – 5 c.	4.5 – 5 c.
Grains	5 oz eq.	5-6 oz eq.	6-7 oz eq.	6-7 oz eq.	7-8 oz eq.	8-9 oz eq.	9-10 oz eq.	10-11 oz eq.
Dairy	2-3 c.	3 c.	3 c.	3 c.	3 c.	3 c.	3 c.	3 c.
Protein	4 oz eq.	5 oz eq.	5-5.5 oz eq.	5.5-6.5 oz eq.	6.5-7 oz eq.	7-7.5 oz eq.	7-7.5 oz eq.	7.5-8 oz eq.
Healthy Oils & Other Fats	4 tsp.	5 tsp.	5 tsp.	6 tsp.	6 tsp.	7 tsp.	8 tsp.	8 tsp.
Water & Super Beverages*	Women: 9 c. Men: 13 c.	Women: 9 c. Men: 13 c.	Women: 9 c. Men: 13 c.	Women: 9 c. Men: 13 c.	Women: 9 c. Men: 13 c.	Women: 9 c. Men: 13 c.	Women: 9 c. Men: 13 c.	Women: 9 c. Men: 13 c.

*May count up to 3 cups caffeinated tea or coffee toward goal

DAILY FOOD GROUP TRACKER

GROUP	FRUITS	VEGETABLES	GRAINS	PROTEIN	DAIRY	HEALTHY OILS & OTHER FATS	WATER & SUPER BEVERAGES
1 Estimate Total							
2 Estimate Total							
3 Estimate Total							
4 Estimate Total							
5 Estimate Total							
6 Estimate Total							
7 Estimate Total							

FOOD CHOICES   DAY ❶

Breakfast: _____
Lunch: _____
Dinner: _____
Snacks: _____

PHYSICAL ACTIVITY   steps/miles/minutes: _____   **SPIRITUAL ACTIVITY**

description: _____   description: _____

FOOD CHOICES

DAY ❷

Breakfast: _____

Lunch: _____

Dinner: _____

Snacks: _____

PHYSICAL ACTIVITY	steps/miles/minutes: _____	SPIRITUAL ACTIVITY

description: _____ | description: _____

FOOD CHOICES

DAY ❸

Breakfast: _____

Lunch: _____

Dinner: _____

Snacks: _____

PHYSICAL ACTIVITY	steps/miles/minutes: _____	SPIRITUAL ACTIVITY

description: _____ | description: _____

FOOD CHOICES

DAY ❹

Breakfast: _____

Lunch: _____

Dinner: _____

Snacks: _____

PHYSICAL ACTIVITY	steps/miles/minutes: _____	SPIRITUAL ACTIVITY

description: _____ | description: _____

FOOD CHOICES

DAY ❺

Breakfast: _____

Lunch: _____

Dinner: _____

Snacks: _____

PHYSICAL ACTIVITY	steps/miles/minutes: _____	SPIRITUAL ACTIVITY

description: _____ | description: _____

FOOD CHOICES

DAY ❻

Breakfast: _____

Lunch: _____

Dinner: _____

Snacks: _____

PHYSICAL ACTIVITY	steps/miles/minutes: _____	SPIRITUAL ACTIVITY

description: _____ | description: _____

FOOD CHOICES

DAY ❼

Breakfast: _____

Lunch: _____

Dinner: _____

Snacks: _____

PHYSICAL ACTIVITY	steps/miles/minutes: _____	SPIRITUAL ACTIVITY

description: _____ | description: _____

LIVE IT TRACKER

Name: _____

Date: _____ Week #: _____

My activity goal for next week:
○ None   ○ <30 min/day   ○ 30-60 min/day

loss/gain _____ Calorie Range: _____

My week at a glance:
○ Great   ○ So-so   ○ Not so great

My food goal for next week: _____
_____

Activity level:
○ None   ○ <30 min/day   ○ 30-60 min/day

RECOMMENDED DAILY AMOUNT OF FOOD FROM EACH GROUP

GROUP	DAILY CALORIES							
	1300-1400	1500-1600	1700-1800	1900-2000	2100-2200	2300-2400	2500-2600	2700-2800
Fruits	1.5 – 2 c.	1.5 – 2 c.	1.5 – 2 c.	2 – 2.5 c.	2 – 2.5 c.	2.5 – 3.5 c.	3.5 – 4.5 c.	3.5 – 4.5 c.
Vegetables	1.5 – 2 c.	2 – 2.5 c.	2.5 – 3 c.	2.5 – 3 c.	3 – 3.5 c.	3.5 – 4.5 c.	4.5 – 5 c.	4.5 – 5 c.
Grains	5 oz eq.	5-6 oz eq.	6-7 oz eq.	6-7 oz eq.	7-8 oz eq.	8-9 oz eq.	9-10 oz eq.	10-11 oz eq.
Dairy	2-3 c.	3 c.	3 c.	3 c.	3 c.	3 c.	3 c.	3 c.
Protein	4 oz eq.	5 oz eq.	5-5.5 oz eq.	5.5-6.5 oz eq.	6.5-7 oz eq.	7-7.5 oz eq.	7-7.5 oz eq.	7.5-8 oz eq.
Healthy Oils & Other Fats	4 tsp.	5 tsp.	5 tsp.	6 tsp.	6 tsp.	7 tsp.	8 tsp.	8 tsp.
Water & Super Beverages*	Women: 9 c. Men: 13 c.	Women: 9 c. Men: 13 c.	Women: 9 c. Men: 13 c.	Women: 9 c. Men: 13 c.	Women: 9 c. Men: 13 c.	Women: 9 c. Men: 13 c.	Women: 9 c. Men: 13 c.	Women: 9 c. Men: 13 c.

*May count up to 3 cups caffeinated tea or coffee toward goal

DAILY FOOD GROUP TRACKER

	GROUP	FRUITS	VEGETABLES	GRAINS	PROTEIN	DAIRY	HEALTHY OILS & OTHER FATS	WATER & SUPER BEVERAGES
1	Estimate Total							
2	Estimate Total							
3	Estimate Total							
4	Estimate Total							
5	Estimate Total							
6	Estimate Total							
7	Estimate Total							

FOOD CHOICES   DAY ❶

Breakfast: _____
Lunch: _____
Dinner: _____
Snacks: _____

PHYSICAL ACTIVITY   steps/miles/minutes: _____

description: _____

SPIRITUAL ACTIVITY

description: _____

FOOD CHOICES

DAY 2

Breakfast: _____

Lunch: _____

Dinner: _____

Snacks: _____

PHYSICAL ACTIVITY   steps/miles/minutes: _____ | **SPIRITUAL ACTIVITY**

description: _____ | description: _____

FOOD CHOICES

DAY 3

Breakfast: _____

Lunch: _____

Dinner: _____

Snacks: _____

PHYSICAL ACTIVITY   steps/miles/minutes: _____ | **SPIRITUAL ACTIVITY**

description: _____ | description: _____

FOOD CHOICES

DAY 4

Breakfast: _____

Lunch: _____

Dinner: _____

Snacks: _____

PHYSICAL ACTIVITY   steps/miles/minutes: _____ | **SPIRITUAL ACTIVITY**

description: _____ | description: _____

FOOD CHOICES

DAY 5

Breakfast: _____

Lunch: _____

Dinner: _____

Snacks: _____

PHYSICAL ACTIVITY   steps/miles/minutes: _____ | **SPIRITUAL ACTIVITY**

description: _____ | description: _____

FOOD CHOICES

DAY 6

Breakfast: _____

Lunch: _____

Dinner: _____

Snacks: _____

PHYSICAL ACTIVITY   steps/miles/minutes: _____ | **SPIRITUAL ACTIVITY**

description: _____ | description: _____

FOOD CHOICES

DAY 7

Breakfast: _____

Lunch: _____

Dinner: _____

Snacks: _____

PHYSICAL ACTIVITY   steps/miles/minutes: _____ | **SPIRITUAL ACTIVITY**

description: _____ | description: _____

LIVE IT TRACKER

Name: _____   Date: _____ Week #: _____

My activity goal for next week: loss / gain _____ Calorie Range: _____

○ None   ○ <30 min/day   ○ 30-60 min/day   My week at a glance:
                                              ○ Great   ○ So-so   ○ Not so great

My food goal for next week: _____   Activity level:
_____   ○ None   ○ <30 min/day   ○ 30-60 min/day

RECOMMENDED DAILY AMOUNT OF FOOD FROM EACH GROUP

GROUP	DAILY CALORIES							
......	1300-1400	1500-1600	1700-1800	1900-2000	2100-2200	2300-2400	2500-2600	2700-2800
Fruits	1.5 – 2 c.	1.5 – 2 c.	1.5 – 2 c.	2 – 2.5 c.	2 – 2.5 c.	2.5 – 3.5 c.	3.5 – 4.5 c.	3.5 – 4.5 c.
Vegetables	1.5 – 2 c.	2 – 2.5 c.	2.5 – 3 c.	2.5 – 3 c.	3 – 3.5 c.	3.5 – 4.5 c..	4.5 – 5 c.	4.5 – 5 c.
Grains	5 oz eq.	5-6 oz eq.	6-7 oz eq.	6-7 oz eq.	7-8 oz eq.	8-9 oz eq.	9-10 oz eq.	10-11 oz eq.
Dairy	2-3 c.	3 c.	3 c.	3 c.	3 c.	3 c.	3 c.	3 c.
Protein	4 oz eq.	5 oz eq.	5-5.5 oz eq.	5.5-6.5 oz eq.	6.5-7 oz eq.	7-7.5 oz eq.	7-7.5 oz eq.	7.5-8 oz eq.
Healthy Oils & Other Fats	4 tsp.	5 tsp.	5 tsp.	6 tsp.	6 tsp.	7 tsp.	8 tsp.	8 tsp.
Water & Super Beverages*	Women: 9 c. Men: 13 c.	Women: 9 c. Men: 13 c.	Women: 9 c. Men: 13 c.	Women: 9 c. Men: 13 c.	Women: 9 c. Men: 13 c.	Women: 9 c. Men: 13 c.	Women: 9 c. Men: 13 c.	Women: 9 c. Men: 13 c.

*May count up to 3 cups caffeinated tea or coffee toward goal

DAILY FOOD GROUP TRACKER

GROUP	FRUITS	VEGETABLES	GRAINS	PROTEIN	DAIRY	HEALTHY OILS & OTHER FATS	WATER & SUPER BEVERAGES
① Estimate Total							
② Estimate Total							
③ Estimate Total							
④ Estimate Total							
⑤ Estimate Total							
⑥ Estimate Total							
⑦ Estimate Total							

FOOD CHOICES   DAY ❶

Breakfast: _____
Lunch: _____
Dinner: _____
Snacks: _____

PHYSICAL ACTIVITY   steps/miles/minutes: _____   **SPIRITUAL ACTIVITY**

description: _____   description: _____

FOOD CHOICES   DAY ❷

Breakfast: _____

Lunch: _____

Dinner: _____

Snacks: _____

PHYSICAL ACTIVITY   steps/miles/minutes: _____   ### SPIRITUAL ACTIVITY

description: _____   description: _____

FOOD CHOICES   DAY ❸

Breakfast: _____

Lunch: _____

Dinner: _____

Snacks: _____

PHYSICAL ACTIVITY   steps/miles/minutes: _____   ### SPIRITUAL ACTIVITY

description: _____   description: _____

FOOD CHOICES   DAY ❹

Breakfast: _____

Lunch: _____

Dinner: _____

Snacks: _____

PHYSICAL ACTIVITY   steps/miles/minutes: _____   ### SPIRITUAL ACTIVITY

description: _____   description: _____

FOOD CHOICES   DAY ❺

Breakfast: _____

Lunch: _____

Dinner: _____

Snacks: _____

PHYSICAL ACTIVITY   steps/miles/minutes: _____   ### SPIRITUAL ACTIVITY

description: _____   description: _____

FOOD CHOICES   DAY ❻

Breakfast: _____

Lunch: _____

Dinner: _____

Snacks: _____

PHYSICAL ACTIVITY   steps/miles/minutes: _____   ### SPIRITUAL ACTIVITY

description: _____   description: _____

FOOD CHOICES   DAY ❼

Breakfast: _____

Lunch: _____

Dinner: _____

Snacks: _____

PHYSICAL ACTIVITY   steps/miles/minutes: _____   ### SPIRITUAL ACTIVITY

description: _____   description: _____

LIVE IT TRACKER

Name: _____   Date: _____ Week #: _____

My activity goal for next week:
○ None   ○ <30 min/day   ○ 30-60 min/day

My food goal for next week: _____

loss/gain _____   Calorie Range: _____

My week at a glance:
○ Great   ○ So-so   ○ Not so great

Activity level:
○ None   ○ <30 min/day   ○ 30-60 min/day

RECOMMENDED DAILY AMOUNT OF FOOD FROM EACH GROUP

GROUP	DAILY CALORIES							
	1300-1400	1500-1600	1700-1800	1900-2000	2100-2200	2300-2400	2500-2600	2700-2800
Fruits	1.5 – 2 c.	1.5 – 2 c.	1.5 – 2 c.	2 – 2.5 c.	2 – 2.5 c.	2.5 – 3.5 c.	3.5 – 4.5 c.	3.5 – 4.5 c.
Vegetables	1.5 – 2 c.	2 – 2.5 c.	2.5 – 3 c.	2.5 – 3 c.	3 – 3.5 c.	3.5 – 4.5 c..	4.5 – 5 c.	4.5 – 5 c.
Grains	5 oz eq.	5-6 oz eq.	6-7 oz eq.	6-7 oz eq.	7-8 oz eq.	8-9 oz eq.	9-10 oz eq.	10-11 oz eq.
Dairy	2-3 c.	3 c.	3 c.	3 c.	3 c.	3 c.	3 c.	3 c.
Protein	4 oz eq.	5 oz eq.	5-5.5 oz eq.	5.5-6.5 oz eq.	6.5-7 oz eq.	7-7.5 oz eq.	7-7.5 oz eq.	7.5-8 oz eq.
Healthy Oils & Other Fats	4 tsp.	5 tsp.	5 tsp.	6 tsp.	6 tsp.	7 tsp.	8 tsp.	8 tsp.
Water & Super Beverages*	Women: 9 c. Men: 13 c.	Women: 9 c. Men: 13 c.	Women: 9 c. Men: 13 c.	Women: 9 c. Men: 13 c.	Women: 9 c. Men: 13 c.	Women: 9 c. Men: 13 c.	Women: 9 c. Men: 13 c.	Women: 9 c. Men: 13 c.

*May count up to 3 cups caffeinated tea or coffee toward goal

DAILY FOOD GROUP TRACKER

GROUP	FRUITS	VEGETABLES	GRAINS	PROTEIN	DAIRY	HEALTHY OILS & OTHER FATS	WATER & SUPER BEVERAGES
1 Estimate Total							
2 Estimate Total							
3 Estimate Total							
4 Estimate Total							
5 Estimate Total							
6 Estimate Total							
7 Estimate Total							

FOOD CHOICES   DAY ❶

Breakfast: _____
Lunch: _____
Dinner: _____
Snacks: _____

PHYSICAL ACTIVITY   steps/miles/minutes: _____
description: _____

SPIRITUAL ACTIVITY
description: _____

FOOD CHOICES

DAY ❷

Breakfast: _____

Lunch: _____

Dinner: _____

Snacks: _____

PHYSICAL ACTIVITY   steps/miles/minutes: _____

description: _____

SPIRITUAL ACTIVITY

description: _____

FOOD CHOICES

DAY ❸

Breakfast: _____

Lunch: _____

Dinner: _____

Snacks: _____

PHYSICAL ACTIVITY   steps/miles/minutes: _____

description: _____

SPIRITUAL ACTIVITY

description: _____

FOOD CHOICES

DAY ❹

Breakfast: _____

Lunch: _____

Dinner: _____

Snacks: _____

PHYSICAL ACTIVITY   steps/miles/minutes: _____

description: _____

SPIRITUAL ACTIVITY

description: _____

FOOD CHOICES

DAY ❺

Breakfast: _____

Lunch: _____

Dinner: _____

Snacks: _____

PHYSICAL ACTIVITY   steps/miles/minutes: _____

description: _____

SPIRITUAL ACTIVITY

description: _____

FOOD CHOICES

DAY ❻

Breakfast: _____

Lunch: _____

Dinner: _____

Snacks: _____

PHYSICAL ACTIVITY   steps/miles/minutes: _____

description: _____

SPIRITUAL ACTIVITY

description: _____

FOOD CHOICES

DAY ❼

Breakfast: _____

Lunch: _____

Dinner: _____

Snacks: _____

PHYSICAL ACTIVITY   steps/miles/minutes: _____

description: _____

SPIRITUAL ACTIVITY

description: _____

LIVE IT TRACKER

Name: _____   Date: _____ Week #: _____

My activity goal for next week: loss / gain _____ Calorie Range: _____
○ None   ○ <30 min/day   ○ 30-60 min/day   My week at a glance:
                                                   ○ Great   ○ So-so   ○ Not so great
My food goal for next week: _____   Activity level:
_____   ○ None   ○ <30 min/day   ○ 30-60 min/day

RECOMMENDED DAILY AMOUNT OF FOOD FROM EACH GROUP

GROUP	DAILY CALORIES							
	1300-1400	1500-1600	1700-1800	1900-2000	2100-2200	2300-2400	2500-2600	2700-2800
Fruits	1.5 – 2 c.	1.5 – 2 c.	1.5 – 2 c.	2 – 2.5 c.	2 – 2.5 c.	2.5 – 3.5 c.	3.5 – 4.5 c.	3.5 – 4.5 c.
Vegetables	1.5 – 2 c.	2 – 2.5 c.	2.5 – 3 c.	2.5 – 3 c.	3 – 3.5 c.	3.5 – 4.5 c..	4.5 – 5 c.	4.5 – 5 c.
Grains	5 oz eq.	5-6 oz eq.	6-7 oz eq.	6-7 oz eq.	7-8 oz eq.	8-9 oz eq.	9-10 oz eq.	10-11 oz eq.
Dairy	2-3 c.	3 c.	3 c.	3 c.	3 c.	3 c.	3 c.	3 c.
Protein	4 oz eq.	5 oz eq.	5-5.5 oz eq.	5.5-6.5 oz eq.	6.5-7 oz eq.	7-7.5 oz eq.	7-7.5 oz eq.	7.5-8 oz eq.
Healthy Oils & Other Fats	4 tsp.	5 tsp.	5 tsp.	6 tsp.	6 tsp.	7 tsp.	8 tsp.	8 tsp.
Water & Super Beverages*	Women: 9 c. Men: 13 c.	Women: 9 c. Men: 13 c.	Women: 9 c. Men: 13 c.	Women: 9 c. Men: 13 c.	Women: 9 c. Men: 13 c.	Women: 9 c. Men: 13 c.	Women: 9 c. Men: 13 c.	Women: 9 c. Men: 13 c.

*May count up to 3 cups caffeinated tea or coffee toward goal

DAILY FOOD GROUP TRACKER

GROUP	FRUITS	VEGETABLES	GRAINS	PROTEIN	DAIRY	HEALTHY OILS & OTHER FATS	WATER & SUPER BEVERAGES
① Estimate Total							
② Estimate Total							
③ Estimate Total							
④ Estimate Total							
⑤ Estimate Total							
⑥ Estimate Total							
⑦ Estimate Total							

FOOD CHOICES   DAY ①

Breakfast: _____
Lunch: _____
Dinner: _____
Snacks: _____

PHYSICAL ACTIVITY   steps/miles/minutes: _____   **SPIRITUAL ACTIVITY**

description: _____   description: _____

FOOD CHOICES

DAY ❷

Breakfast: _____
Lunch: _____
Dinner: _____
Snacks: _____

PHYSICAL ACTIVITY   steps/miles/minutes: _____

description: _____

SPIRITUAL ACTIVITY

description: _____

FOOD CHOICES

DAY ❸

Breakfast: _____
Lunch: _____
Dinner: _____
Snacks: _____

PHYSICAL ACTIVITY   steps/miles/minutes: _____

description: _____

SPIRITUAL ACTIVITY

description: _____

FOOD CHOICES

DAY ❹

Breakfast: _____
Lunch: _____
Dinner: _____
Snacks: _____

PHYSICAL ACTIVITY   steps/miles/minutes: _____

description: _____

SPIRITUAL ACTIVITY

description: _____

FOOD CHOICES

DAY ❺

Breakfast: _____
Lunch: _____
Dinner: _____
Snacks: _____

PHYSICAL ACTIVITY   steps/miles/minutes: _____

description: _____

SPIRITUAL ACTIVITY

description: _____

FOOD CHOICES

DAY ❻

Breakfast: _____
Lunch: _____
Dinner: _____
Snacks: _____

PHYSICAL ACTIVITY   steps/miles/minutes: _____

description: _____

SPIRITUAL ACTIVITY

description: _____

FOOD CHOICES

DAY ❼

Breakfast: _____
Lunch: _____
Dinner: _____
Snacks: _____

PHYSICAL ACTIVITY   steps/miles/minutes: _____

description: _____

SPIRITUAL ACTIVITY

description: _____

100-MILE CLUB

WALKING			
slowly, 2 mph	30 min =	156 cal =	1 mile
moderately, 3 mph	20 min =	156 cal =	1 mile
very briskly, 4 mph	15 min =	156 cal =	1 mile
speed walking	10 min =	156 cal =	1 mile
up stairs	13 min =	159 cal =	1 mile
RUNNING / JOGGING			
• • •	10 min =	156 cal =	1 mile
CYCLE OUTDOORS			
slowly, < 10 mph	20 min =	156 cal =	1 mile
light effort, 10-12 mph	12 min =	156 cal =	1 mile
moderate effort, 12-14 mph	10 min =	156 cal =	1 mile
vigorous effort, 14-16 mph	7.5 min =	156 cal =	1 mile
very fast, 16-19 mph	6.5 min =	152 cal =	1 mile
SPORTS ACTIVITIES			
playing tennis (singles)	10 min =	156 cal =	1 mile
swimming			
light to moderate effort	11 min =	152 cal =	1 mile
fast, vigorous effort	7.5 min =	156 cal =	1 mile
softball	15 min =	156 cal =	1 mile
golf	20 min =	156 cal =	1 mile
rollerblading	6.5 min =	152 cal =	1 mile
ice skating	11 min =	152 cal =	1 mile
jumping rope	7.5 min =	156 cal =	1 mile
basketball	12 min =	156 cal =	1 mile
soccer (casual)	15 min =	159 min =	1 mile
AROUND THE HOUSE			
mowing grass	22 min =	156 cal =	1 mile
mopping, sweeping, vacuuming	19.5 min =	155 cal =	1 mile
cooking	40 min =	160 cal =	1 mile
gardening	19 min =	156 cal =	1 mile
housework (general)	35 min =	156 cal =	1 mile

AROUND THE HOUSE			
ironing	45 min =	153 cal =	1 mile
raking leaves	25 min =	150 cal =	1 mile
washing car	23 min =	156 cal =	1 mile
washing dishes	45 min =	153 cal =	1 mile
AT THE GYM			
stair machine	8.5 min =	155 cal =	1 mile
stationary bike			
slowly, 10 mph	30 min =	156 cal =	1 mile
moderately, 10-13 mph	15 min =	156 cal =	1 mile
vigorously, 13-16 mph	7.5 min =	156 cal =	1 mile
briskly, 16-19 mph	6.5 min =	156 cal =	1 mile
elliptical trainer	12 min =	156 cal =	1 mile
weight machines (vigorously)	13 min =	152 cal =	1 mile
aerobics			
low impact	15 min =	156 cal =	1 mile
high impact	12 min =	156 cal =	1 mile
water	20 min =	156 cal =	1 mile
pilates	15 min =	156 cal =	1 mile
raquetball (casual)	15 min =	156 cal =	1 mile
stretching exercises	25 min =	150 cal =	1 mile
weight lifting (also works for weight machines used moderately or gently)	30 min =	156 cal =	1 mile
FAMILY LEISURE			
playing piano	37 min =	155 cal =	1 mile
jumping rope	10 min =	152 cal =	1 mile
skating (moderate)	20 min =	152 cal =	1 mile
swimming			
moderate	17 min =	156 cal =	1 mile
vigorous	10 min =	148 cal =	1 mile
table tennis	25 min =	150 cal =	1 mile
walk / run / play with kids	25 min =	150 cal =	1 mile

Let's Count Our Miles!

Color each circle to represent a mile you've completed.
Watch your progress to that 100 mile marker!

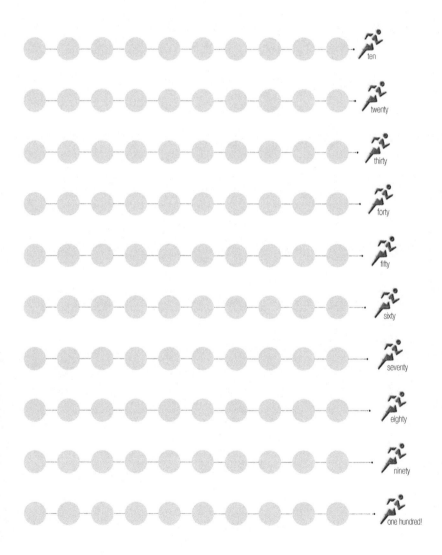

Made in the USA
Monee, IL
20 September 2023

43011893R00122